4 Weeks to Total Energy

4 Weeks to Total Energy

Judith Wills

Photography by Sandra Lousada

Quadrille

To all those energy-givers in my life
who have helped me find mine

First published in 2000 by
Quadrille Publishing Limited
Alhambra House
27–31 Charing Cross Road
London WC2H OLS

Cataloguing in Publication Data: a catalogue record for this book
is available from the British Library

ISBN 1 902757 18 1 (paperback)
ISBN 1 902757 70 X (hardback)

Printed in Germany

contents

What exactly is energy? When I began work on this book I asked everyone I met for their definition of the word, and didn't get the same reply twice. Below are some of the answers I was given.

introduction

'being able to work hard all day long without feeling tired' ... 'physical stamina' ... **'zest for life'** ... 'mental motivation' ... **'drive'** ... 'enthusiasm' ... **'that get-up-and-go feeling'** ... 'feeling fit and healthy' ... **'the absence of tiredness or lethargy'** ... 'clear-headedness' ... **'enjoyment of life'** ... 'the ability to make the most of yourself and your life'

Energy is all of those things, but of these definitions I was given I find the last one comes nearest to my understanding of what it really is. You can be clever, you can be talented, you can be lucky, you can be good-looking, you can be loved and committed – but none of these gifts can be maximised without energy.

So is energy just the icing on the cake then? Something that makes all that you have even better? No, because icing is frivolous and a luxury, not really needed. Energy IS needed. Energy is perhaps more important than all the other attributes put together. Without energy you may well be unable to use many or any of your other gifts and your life will be, at least in part, wasted.

MY DEFINITION OF ENERGY IS THE PERSONAL LIFE FORCE WHICH ENABLES YOU TO MAXIMIZE YOUR POTENTIAL IN EVERY AREA.

Whatever your plans or ideas, hopes or dreams, without the energy to begin them and to see them through, you have nothing.

Energy is your power base. If you currently feel as though your life is a long incline and you have nothing but a rusty push-bike to help you along, think of total energy as being powered through life with the help of a smooth 4-litre engine.

Energy isn't just about absence of negative feelings – lack of tiredness, lack of lethargy – but about being positive, full of enthusiasm and life and hope.

But energy isn't simply 'a gift', because the word gift implies something you may not ever be fortunate enough to come by;

something you either have or don't have and there is little you can do to alter that fact.

I believe that YOU can make your own energy. Total energy does not come from just one area but from several, each of which should be within your grasp.

You can increase your capacity and well-being in every aspect – physical, mental, emotional, relationships, career, earnings, playtime – if you increase your energy.

This book, FOUR WEEKS TO TOTAL ENERGY, shows you how to maximize your own energy potential and live your life to the full, in four simple and logical steps. Whatever your age, you can do it.

This IS your life – make the most of it, starting NOW.

The energy balance

Total energy is synergistic – it comes from a variety of sources and all these sources should work together to produce the perfect 'whole'. That is what we will be aiming for in this book.

Many people have areas of outstanding energy but not the true energy balance. For example, a research scientist who regularly works a 12-hour day, seven days a week, for months on end, while trying to resolve an important problem, has extremely well-developed mental energy, but show him a hill to climb or ask him to stay late at a party and he has no energy at all.

Then there is the athlete who trains as hard for much of the year to win medals as the scientist works to solve his problem. His physical energy is near the top of the table, but ask him to read a book or cook a meal and he may not have the energy to do that.

And indeed, both the scientist and the athlete may find that when the problem is solved or the athletic season over, long months of energy burn-out and exhaustion follow – for energy is rarely UNLIMITED unless it is BALANCED.

However, there are many people who, for reasons of physical or emotional ill-health, may be unable to achieve the perfect balance of energy. Even with such limitations you can still use the programme to improve your own optimum energy levels. My role model here is Stephen Hawking, the theoretical physicist who spends his life in a wheelchair, physically incapacitated to a huge degree with motor neurone disease, and yet has the kind of mental and intellectual energy that you and I can only dream about.

For the majority of us, though, the trick is to analyse our weak energy areas and learn how to improve them in a synergistic way. This is the theory behind the Chinese concept of yin and yang, which aims to produce a perfect flow of chi – energy. You do this by encouraging the energy-givers into your life and discouraging the energy-takers.

The energy-givers and takers

- Good health gives energy. Poor health can take it away.
- The right level of relaxation gives energy. Tension drains it.
- Physical fitness gives energy. Lack of fitness gets in its way.
- Good diet gives energy. Poor diet saps energy.
- Good sleep gives energy. Lack of adequate rest and sleep disrupts it.
- Good air gives energy. Poor air prevents it.
- Balance in body and mind gives energy. An unbalanced lifestyle dilutes it.
- Good environment gives energy. Unsympathetic surroundings block it.
- Positive emotions give energy. Negative emotions exhaust it.
- Self-regard gives energy. Low self-esteem is enervating.

The four steps to total energy

Maybe you've tried to improve your energy levels before and haven't met with much success. Perhaps you feel tired too much of the time and so you've cut down on alcohol and get to bed earlier – but you still don't feel much better. Or perhaps you have taken up exercise to try to cope with stress and burn-out at work, but feel even more tired now than you did before.

The way to total energy is to approach it logically, as you would if building your own house, which is the analogy I use throughout the book. What you will be doing if you follow this programme is building energy step by step in a way that is right for you and that works for everyone. Each of the four steps in the book represents approximately 25 per cent of your total energy quotient and so you need to carry out all these steps in order to reach your maximum energy potential.

Step 1

gets you Back to Basics – clearing and levelling the 'site' and building strong foundations. It recognizes that you can't build energy on negative stress and physical and mental tension. It aims to clear your mind and body and provide you with a firm base from which to proceed.

Step 2

finds your optimum level of Physical Energy – creating the shell of the 'building' with strong walls and sound construction. It shows you how to eat and drink, how to build physical strength and stamina and how to oxygenate and give life to your body.

Step 3
shows you how to Control the Chaos in your life that is blocking your energy. Think of this as designing a state-of-the-art control centre in your building so that everything runs smoothly and efficiently. This step helps you to train your brain to take the right decisions to conserve and create energy every day.

Step 4
helps you to Push Back the Boundaries and open your mind. Having 'put your home in order', think of this step as where you begin to discover, or rediscover, the world outside your door – and, of course, the potential within your mind. Step 4 shows you how to use your new-found energy in a positive way to create even more energy and fulfilment in your life.

How to use this book

Simply start at the beginning, first doing the Energy Quotient questionnaires overleaf and then working logically through the steps. The Index will lead you immediately to areas of particular interest, but it is important to follow the programme according to the four logical Steps.

To help you, there is a 4-week programme, one week of which appears at the beginning of each Step, if you want to use it. It gives a structured plan for you to follow to help you increase your energy levels in just 28 days. However, you may well need more time than this to find your own total energy level – everyone will vary.

There is also a 3-day plan at the back of the book which you can use either as a taster of what the full programme is about, or to refresh yourself in the future. This plan needs three days off work, but you can work while using much of the 28-day plan.

I designed this programme because following similar principles worked for me. I am sure they will work for you too, and I that you will enjoy yourself while building your own 'energy powerhouse'. Do write and let me know how you get on.

You and your own energy levels

Before you begin the four-step programme, you need to take a long hard look at yourself and your life with the help of these Energy Quotient questionnaires. They will enable you to work out how good – or how poor – your energy levels are, and in which areas you most need to improve.

How are your own energy levels right now? If you are reading this book you probably feel that they are low, but how low are they? Do you have good and bad energy areas? The questionnaires will help you to assess your own energy quotient and then I offer guidance on what your score means and how best to act on the information it provides.

The first questionnaire looks at your Physical Energy – how your body copes with the demands your lifestyle places on it. The second looks at Mental Energy – how your mind faces and deals with your life and all the activity you ask it to perform.

Answer each question as honestly as possible. There are no wrong answers, but if you build up a false picture of your own energy levels by not giving what you know is a true answer, you will only be misleading yourself. To answer the questions, all you do is circle the number that you feel most closely corresponds to the right answer for you. 1 is the lowest/poorest score you can give to an answer; 10 is the highest/best.

Energy quotient questionnaire 1

Physical Energy

1 Evaluate how you feel physically at the time you are about to get up out of bed in the morning. Circle your energy levels.
(1 = no energy at all, want to stay in bed; 10 = feel great, want to leap out of bed and get on with the day)

1 2 3 4 5 6 7 8 9 10

2 Think about how you feel most days in the early afternoon, when you are at work. Circle the number that most closely corresponds to your physical feeling.
(1 = sluggish, tired, slow; 10 = full of energy and life)

1 2 3 4 5 6 7 8 9 10

3 Think about when you walk around at work, even if it is just a little. How much energy do you put into your movement around your place of work? Circle a number that fits in best.
(1 = hardly any movement and when you do have to walk you do it slowly, and never walk up stairs if there is a lift available; and 10 = you move around a lot, going as fast as you can, running up stairs and so on)

1 2 3 4 5 6 7 8 9 10

4 Think about when you get home from work. What are you most likely to do at that time? Circle your energy levels.
(1 = slump down into a chair and take a long rest – or feel like doing so; 10 = go out for a jog or begin on some gardening)

1 2 3 4 5 6 7 8 9 10

5 Think about physical work you have to do at home, say, making beds or ironing or lifting boxes. Circle the number that most closely corresponds to how you feel, more often than not, when you have to do physical chores.
(1 = weak, tired, find doing physical chores very hard; 10 = it's easy, no problem, could carry on for ages)

1 2 3 4 5 6 7 8 9 10

6 Sometimes we all need to speed up considerably for a few seconds – running for the train or rushing up a flight of stairs when we're late for a meeting. If you do, how are you likely to feel?
(1 = completely out of breath, with wobbly legs and pounding heart, taking a while to recover; 10 = no problem, you feel absolutely fine)

1 2 3 4 5 6 7 8 9 10

7 You go out for a long walk with friends. How would you rate your progress compared with the others?
(1 = not able to keep up, have to rest a lot, can't talk while walking; 10 = impatient because no one can keep up with you, as you are such a fast walker)

1 2 3 4 5 6 7 8 9 10

8 Think about how many hours a day you are physically active. Rate yourself on the scale.
(1 = little or no activity, sit or lie down mostly if given the choice; 10 = on the go most of the day if given the choice)

1 2 3 4 5 6 7 8 9 10

9 Think about how long you spend in bed. Rate yourself on the scale.
(1 = you get up late and go to bed early every day; 10 = you get up early and go to bed quite late every day)

1 2 3 4 5 6 7 8 9 10

10 Look at yourself in the mirror in the middle of a typical day for you. Rate yourself on your perceived vitality.
(1 = dull eyes, dark circles, pallor; 10 = bright eye whites and sparkling eyes, lively expression, good skin tone and colour)

1 2 3 4 5 6 7 8 9 10

11 Think about your perfect holiday and what it would involve, assuming that you are physically capable of carrying out your chosen holiday. Rate your choice on the scale.
(1 = nothing but lazing on the beach sipping cocktails and reading the occasional magazine; 10 = a trekking holiday in the Himalayas – carrying your own backpack, of course)

1 2 3 4 5 6 7 8 9 10

12 How many physically active hobbies do you have and enjoy? Think about it then give your answer.
(1 = none; 10 = several, undertaken regularly, from football to cycling to swimming and gardening or similar)

1 2 3 4 5 6 7 8 9 10

NOW Add up the numbers you have circled for the 12 physical energy questions and write your score here:
My physical energy total score is ☐ BOX 1

NOW add up the numbers you have circled in questions 1–6 and 7–12 separately and write your scores here:
My physical energy score for questions 1–6 is ☐ BOX 2
My physical energy score for questions 7–12 is ☐ BOX 3

Energy quotient questionnaire 2

Mental energy

1 Do you seek out and enjoy conversation with people whom you perceive to be more knowledgeable/intellectual than you? Circle your score.
(1 = not at all; 10 = yes, as often as possible)

1 2 3 4 5 6 7 8 9 10

2 If someone makes a wisecrack at your expense how would you do on the witty one-liner reply or put-down?
(1 = can never think of anything to say until later, if at all; 10 = I am never short of an instant, witty reply)

1 2 3 4 5 6 7 8 9 10

3 The in-tray is empty, you're completely up to date with work and have no worries. What is likely to happen next?
(1 = you switch off completely for as long as life lets you; 10 = ideas, plans, thoughts keep coming into your mind, you just can't help it)

1 2 3 4 5 6 7 8 9 10

4 Browsing through a newspaper you spy a crossword or brain-teaser puzzle not done. What are you likely to do?
(1 = turn the page quickly – such things don't interest you at all; 10 = find a pen and start scribbling, not finishing till all solutions are found)

1 2 3 4 5 6 7 8 9 10

5 You arrive at a function and are introduced to a dozen new people. How are you likely to do on remembering their names next time you meet them?
(1 = wouldn't know their names or their faces either;
10 = would remember all of them)

1 2 3 4 5 6 7 8 9 10

6 It's a busy day. You're on the phone, trying to cook a meal or write a report, write a shopping list and pacify a colleague (or kids) all at the same time. How do you cope?
(1 = burst into tears, fake a fainting fit or scream at everyone;
10 = that's an easy moment, I've coped with far worse)

1 2 3 4 5 6 7 8 9 10

7 You're writing a long and slightly tedious report/essay which is going to take many hours of effort to finish. Think about how hard you concentrate on the task in hand.
(1=you drift off on to another subject or you spend long periods gazing out of the window; 10 =you allow no distractions at all until finished)

1 2 3 4 5 6 7 8 9 10

8 When choosing reading matter for pleasure how deep or how light do you like it to be?
(an example of 1 might be a highly illustrated book on your favourite hobby and 10 = James Joyce's Ulysses*)*

1 2 3 4 5 6 7 8 9 10

9 Think about outstanding jobs there are to do at home, e.g. painting, mending, gardening. How long do chores on average have to wait before you do them?
(1 = all the chores have been waiting for six months or more; 10 = I do chores as soon as I have decided that they need doing)

1 2 3 4 5 6 7 8 9 10

10 Think about your future. Do you have a good idea pretty far ahead of how you want it to be?
(1 = I live in the present, never planning even for tomorrow;
10 = definitely – you need to think about the future in order for it to stand the best chance of working out how you'd like)

1 2 3 4 5 6 7 8 9 10

11 Once you have an idea – say, about a special holiday or a business plan for work – how strong is your compunction to see it through to the end? Circle your answer.
(1 = I get ideas but leave it to others to see them through, or discard them; 10 = I always put my ideas into action and see them through)

1 2 3 4 5 6 7 8 9 10

12 Someone asks you to organize a big party for a relative or a special event. Think about your attitude to this and what happens next.
(1 = no one would ask me as they know how bad I am at organizing anything at all; 10 = you're writing lists and on the phone straight away and won't rest until the last guest has gone home)

1 2 3 4 5 6 7 8 9 10

NOW add up the numbers you have circled for the 12 mental energy questions and write down the total here:

My mental energy quotient is ☐ BOX 4

NOW add up the numbers you have circled in questions 1–6 and 7–12 separately and write your scores here:
My mental energy score for questions 1–6 is ☐ BOX 5

My mental energy score for questions 7–12 is ☐ BOX 6

FINALLY ADD TOGETHER the two scores for the complete set of physical energy and mental energy questionnaires (Boxes 1 and 4) and write the total here:
BOX 1+BOX 4 ☐ THIS IS YOUR TOTAL ENERGY QUOTIENT

Your scores and what they mean

Your total energy quotient

IF YOUR COMBINED SCORE FOR BOXES 1 AND 4 IS:

60 or under You have very poor total energy and need to work at the complete programme to improve your energy levels.

61–120: You have poor-to-moderate total energy and will benefit greatly from the programme in this book. Both mental and physical energy are probably poor, but check your individual scores for both these below for further advice.

121–180 You have moderate-to-average energy levels. You get by quite well, but there are several areas for improvement. Check individual scores on physical and mental energy for further advice.

181–240 You have good-to-excellent energy levels. The nearer your score is to 240, the less likely it is that you really need this book! However, if your score is at the lower end of this section, it is worth checking your individual physical and mental energy scores. Your energy may be unbalanced; you may have good physical energy but less good mental energy, or vice versa. In that case you need to work on your poorer areas as described below.

Physical energy quotient (Box 1)

30 or under You have very low physical energy and need to pay particular attention to all the advice in Step 2.

31–60 You have low physical energy and need to work on all the advice in Step 2. Look at your total score for questions 1–6 (Box 2) compared with your total score for questions 7–12 (Box 3). Are they similar or is one high and the other low? A very low score in 1–6 indicates poor short-term physical energy; you need to work on muscular strength and lung capacity. A very low score in 7–12 indicates poor long-term energy; you need to work on stamina and strength, plus diet.

61–90 You have moderate-to-average physical energy. Don't sit back and do nothing – there is room for improvement. See suggestions for 31–60.

91–120 You have good-to-excellent physical energy. If your score is at the higher end, you need do nothing other than maintain current levels of physical energy. At the lower end, there may still be room for improvement, especially if your scores in the first and second halves of the questionnaire were unbalanced – see suggestions for low first- or second-half scores above.

Mental energy quotient (Box 4)

30 or under You have very low mental energy and it is important to work hard on Steps 3 and 4 of the programme, even though it may not look like the kind of work you like to do.

31–60 You have low mental energy – work carefully on Steps 3 and 4 of the programme when you have completed Steps 1 and 2. Compare your scores for the first half (Box 5) and second half (Box 6) of the mental energy questionnaire. Are they very unbalanced? A low score in the first half indicates poor short-term mental energy and you could benefit from extra work on Step 3, particularly the exercises in harmony, efficiency and stress relief. A low score in the second half indicates poor long-term mental energy and you could benefit from extra time spent on the Mental Stamina exercise in Step 3, as well as the whole of Step 4. Don't forget that poor physical fitness and health can also affect mental energy, so take all the advice in Step 2.

61–90 You have moderate-to-average mental energy and taking steps to improve it will increase your overall enthusiasm for life tremendously. Read the comments for the 31–60 score and commit yourself to the programme.

91–120 You have good-to-excellent mental energy. The higher your score, the less likely it is that you need to improve your mental energy. However, if your score in the mental energy questionnaire was unbalanced, with a much lower score in either questions 1–6 or 7–12, follow the advice given above (see score 31–60) for low first- or second-half scores.

step 1

Getting Back to Basics

Clearing your body and mind to give yourself a clean start

Let's face it – you are carrying around with you an awful lot of junk that you don't need or want... in your brain, in your muscles, in your nerves, in your body and mind. You are carrying a physical and mental burden of rubbish accumulated over the years which is slowing you down as well as winding you up. You cannot begin to increase your energy levels until you get rid of that rubbish. You need to make a 'clean start' – and that is what Step 1 is all about.

In Step 1 you will rid yourself of the basic energy-blockers and learn to detox and relax both your mind and your body, releasing long-term emotion and tension and leaving yourself free to move on.

In building terms, this is what some people would consider the 'boring' stage – clearing and levelling the site and making strong foundations. However, as all builders will tell you, it is the most important stage of any construction. Rather than feeling bored, by the end of it I am sure that you will feel clear-headed, relaxed and eager for change, ready for the Steps that follow.

We will do this clearing by calling upon various tried and tested relaxation and detox techniques adapted from therapies and methods both old and new, from all corners of the world.

These methods range from massage, breathing and postural techniques through stretching, muscle relaxation therapies, basic yoga and meditation, to self-calming techniques such as audiotherapy and hydrotherapy, and detoxing through diet.

We also look at your sleep patterns and their relationship with energy, and we examine the Sloth Syndrome – when you're tired all the time – and learn how to eliminate it.

You don't have to try out all the techniques yourself but pick the ones that seem most appropriate to you, with our help. First read through the whole of Step 1, making notes on techniques that are practical for you as you do so. Turn the page for a suggested plan of action for week 1 of the programme. You may take as long as you like over this stage – a week may not be long enough if your own personal 'junkload' is too heavy.

Try to pick a quiet week in your life to start this Step. The more time you can devote to it, the better. You're going to get right back to basics.

Unwind. Relax. It will happen. Step 1 is the key.

Four-week programme

The four-week programme – one week of which is to be found at the beginning of each step, as here – is intended as a suggested schedule for a logical progression through the four steps to Total Energy. Four weeks is the minimum time you should allow for completing the steps – for many people it may take longer to work through them adequately. However, you can still use the programme as a guide, simply increasing the time given for each area, to suit yourself. For example, you may like to take two weeks to cover each step, or even four. You should use this programme in conjunction with the detailed information given throughout the book – you are referred to page numbers as necessary. For some sections, a note-pad and pen, or computer, will be useful.

Week 1

General notes

It will be helpful if this is a quiet week for you – if employed, you may like to plan this week to coincide with time off.

Day 1

- Do the Energy Quotient Questionnaires (pages 10–15) to work out your own energy levels and make a note to give more time to your weaker areas in the weeks ahead.
- Read through all of Step 1.
- Try to relax as much as possible today.

Day 2

- Clear out your larder and fridge, and shop for the Detox diet (pages 52–54).
- Begin the Detox Diet.
- Do the How Wound Up Are You? quiz and consider the results.
- Have a massage, either self- or partner-given (pages 25–32).
- Rest and relax – perhaps with music – for the rest of the day.

Day 3

- Go through the complete breathing and posture sections (pages 32–5), practising the techniques outlined there. Practise daily from now on.
- Take a gentle walk for 30 minutes, somewhere quiet if possible.

Day 4

- Begin the stretching routine (pages 36–7). Do the Long Body Stretch (page 37) 2 or 3 times today. Do your stretches most days from now on, particularly when you feel tense.

Day 5

- Read through the section on relaxation methods again (pages 42–3) and see which methods you feel may help you. Begin to practise them.
- Do the facial exercises to release tension from the face (page 23).

Day 6

- Take time to look at your quality and patterns of sleep and rest. Think about your levels of tiredness with the help of pages 44–51. Begin to take some of the suggestions on board.

Day 7

- Try a sequence of the Sun Salutation yoga poses (pages 40–41). Aim to improve your technique on this over the weeks ahead, doing the sequence 4–5 times a week and building up repeats.
- Consider also Pilates/Alexander technique for body balancing (see page 35 and the Appendix).
- Read the Step 1 Round-up (page 55).

TURN THE PAGE TO START STEP ONE

How wound up are you?
12 ways to tell

The more tightly wound you are with the stresses and strains of your life, the longer it takes to unwind and get your mind and body back to that 'clear site' state for which we're aiming.

Just how wound up are you? A little, or a lot?

Answer yes or no to the following:

		YES	NO
1	Are you quick to take offence and / or misinterpret remarks people make about you in a negative way?	○	○
2	Do you often use aggressive behaviour – such as starting arguments, raising your voice – or have outbursts of temper for little reason?	○	○
3	Are you slow to forget or forgive minor transgressions on the part of others and do you make 'mountains out of molehills'?	○	○
4	Do you suffer from regular chronic muscular pain unrelated to over-exercise?	○	○
5	Is your jaw clenched tight together at this moment, with teeth tight shut?	○	○
6	Do you have difficulty sleeping or have poor quality of sleep, often interrupted by fits of anxious wakefulness?	○	○
7	When you are trying to relax do you find it hard to stop your brain from turning recent events or problems over and over?	○	○
8	Do you need alcohol, drugs, cigarettes or other types of addictive aids to help you relax?	○	○

9 Do you have trouble concentrating on the written word and find yourself going over the same piece several times? ○ ○

10 Do you suffer frequent mood swings, with anger, acute depression or sadness coming on for no reason you can later pin down? ○ ○

11 Do you suffer regularly from digestive disorders of any kind? ○ ○

12 Do you suffer from skin complaints, e.g. eczema, spots, high colour? ○ ○

10 or more 'yes's: If you answered 'yes' to 10 or more of these questions you are very wound up indeed ... like a tightly coiled spring. Don't mistake this for positive energy. It isn't – it is very negative. You probably spend a great deal of your time feeling mentally and physically exhausted. You really do need to clear your mind and body, relax and wind right down. We can lessen the tension of the spring gradually throughout Step 1 so that you can then carry on to improve your energy levels in the rest of the programme.

5–9 'yes's: You are far too tense and wound up to be able to find true energy yet. Use Step 1 to help you relax and detox then you will be able to tackle your energy problems and cure them in the long term.

1–4 'yes's: You are fairly relaxed about life, but there is quite probably room for improvement, as modern living poses stresses on even the most equitable of temperaments. If you feel your energy levels are low, you do need to relax even more.

No 'yes's at all: It could be that you are in denial and mistaking the Sloth Syndrome (see page 47) for genuine calm and relaxation. Read that page and take on board the comments.

1

True relaxation is a holistic affair. Here we take a look at its various components and show how you can achieve these through simple exercise, stretch, breathing, massage and yoga techniques.

learn to relax

deep relaxation is the first step towards total energy

Instant relaxers

Try these eight instant – or almost instant – ways to relieve and relax physical and mental tension and stress if you scored very high on the How Wound Up Are You? quiz. They will help you to relax enough to get into the more detailed programme that follows.

Do any or all of them whenever you can fit them in – or when you most feel the need – throughout the day.

1 SHORT BURST OF AEROBIC EXERCISE that will make you feel slightly 'puffed' but not gasping. This could be a 3-minute walk or step session, a short skip or running up and down stairs. Suit the activity to your own fitness level (for more information on safe aerobic exercise see pages 81–7). This will help to disperse adrenalin and calm you down, especially after any type of emotional conflict.

2 SELF-MASSAGE is extremely helpful in reducing muscle tension build-up on the face, around the eyes and in the neck and scalp (see pages 29–32). Spend 2–3 minutes on this twice a day if possible.

3 FACIAL EXERCISE is an alternative, or addition, to self-massage. Start by yawning as deeply as you can. It doesn't matter if you have to fake the yawn, it is the movement that achieves instant relaxation of the face. Now see the panel opposite for three quick exercises that will relax the facial muscles, tone up the face and calm you down. Again, repeat once or twice a day.

4 RELAX AND VISUALIZE. Sit in a comfortable chair with your head slightly back and the eyes shut. If there is a lot of tension around the eyes it will help them to relax if you wear a blackout mask or cool gel-filled mask (available from chemists). Sigh deeply and then breathe slowly throughout the rest of this exercise. Picture a predetermined scene that you know will help you feel tranquil, e.g. a summer's day in a park or on a beach, or lying in bed listening to music. Put yourself in the scene. If other thoughts come into your mind, try to banish them. It may help if you recite a poem or sing along to the music in your mind. Do this for at least 3 minutes.

5 THE LONG BODY STRETCH is a 2-minute lying stretch that relaxes both your shoulders and your spine and also helps to calm your spirit. See page 37. If you're in a situation where you can't lie down, you can do a long half-body stretch sitting down by raising your arms up above your head, with shoulders down and back, and breathing deeply and quietly for 1 minute.

Facial exercises

(See 3 opposite) For each of these exercises, sit upright in a supportive chair with your head, neck and shoulders as relaxed as possible, but keeping good posture.

1 Open your mouth as wide as you can, then stick your tongue out as far as it will go and open your eyes as wide as you can. Relax and repeat 10 times. This is not a pretty sight, so turn your back to any audience you may have.

2 Slowly tip your head back to stretch the front of the neck. When you feel a good stretch, let your mouth drop open – your jaw will relax completely. Now bring your tongue up so that its middle area hits the roof of your mouth, then return to the starting position. Repeat this 10 times. Apart from relaxing your jaw, this exercise will also tone your jaw-line and neck.

3 Purse your lips into a small circle (as if you are about to kiss someone you don't really like), really pushing the lips out into that round shape. Relax and smile. Repeat 10 times. This will relax and tone your mouth area and relax the area under your eyes.

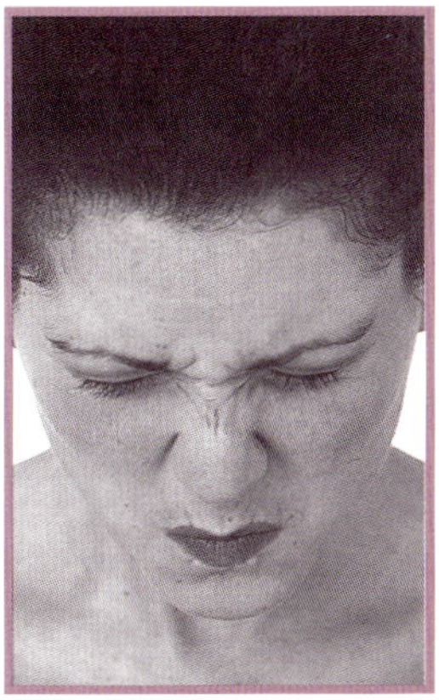

6 DEEPER BREATHING. When you are tense or stressed, your breathing tends to be too shallow and this will exacerbate the problem. A minute or two of concentrated deeper, slower breathing will help to restore your calm and clear your mind. Try to sit in a chair that allows you to adopt good posture, or stand, near an open window if possible. Breathe following the guidelines on pages 32–3.

7 CHANTING. You may not be able to do this in an open-plan office or on the train, but you can certainly do it at home or anywhere where you can have a couple of minutes to yourself. Sit or stand as in previous exercise and chant a previously chosen phrase or word that makes you feel good and calm about yourself and which also makes a soothing sound when repeated in a low, slow voice. There are some ideas on page 39.

8 NECK AND SHOULDER EXERCISE. Sitting for long hours slumped over a desk, in an uncomfortable chair, or at a work-station, can give you muscular-imbalance-related neck and shoulder tension which will build up lactic acid and add to stress. Help disperse this lactic acid with a few minutes of neck and shoulder exercise.

Neck exercises

(See 8 above) For each of these exercises, sit in a supportive chair with your head, neck and shoulder muscles as relaxed as possible, but keeping good posture.

❶ Stretching to the left and then to the right will relax both sides of the neck and the tops of the shoulders.

❷ Slowly drawing the chin down towards your chest will help to relax your upper spine and the back of the neck.

Try to sit (or stand) in as good a posture as possible (for more tips on good posture turn to pages 32–5). Breathe gently and naturally and move your head to the left and down, stretching the right side of the neck, then slowly turn to the right and down, stretching the left side. Bring your chin down towards your chest to stretch the back of the neck. Now bring your shoulders back and down and, with your arms loosely at your sides, shrug your shoulders up towards your ears and back down again. Repeat several times. Try to do this every hour while sitting.

The power of massage

The two major effects we want to achieve in Step 1 are physical and mental relaxation and release, paving the way for mind and body self-awareness. Perhaps THE very best therapy for achieving all this is body massage.

With massage you are doing far more than simply mobilizing or relaxing aching muscles. Ample research has demonstrated that massage can have far-reaching effects in reducing stress levels, in lowering blood pressure, relieving pain, strengthening the immune system, improving circulation, unlocking repressed emotions and increasing energy.

Most of us hold our muscles in a permanent state of tension that draws on our energy reserves and prevents real relaxation. Give your body a moment's thought NOW. Are your shoulders tensed upwards? Stomach knotted and tight? Breath locked into a tight diaphragm? Toes curled up, fingers clenched? These are all signs of tense muscles and this is almost always directly related to stress. You need to work on relaxing those muscles straight away while we gradually get the stress problems sorted out too.

For this reason we start getting back to basics with an immediate programme of daily massage. If you can afford professional massage that is good, but massage from your partner (you can reciprocate) is more than adequate as the basic massage techniques are easy to learn. If neither of these is an option, quite a lot can easily be achieved with self-massage, using your own hands and/or a massage machine.

A good basic massage

Allow a minimum of 30 minutes, plus resting time, for the person being massaged. This is long enough to give a fairly thorough back-of-body massage. For a full-body massage you need to allow up to an hour, but inexperienced masseurs may well feel tired – with aching fingers, etc. – long before that. Vary this routine to suit both of you – as long as the recipient finds it pleasant and relaxing that is fine.

• The person to be massaged should lie on their stomach in a warm room on a very firm bed or mattress, or on the floor with a thick layer of towel or duvet underneath them, unclothed, with a blanket or large towels to cover up areas not being worked on. Head and knees can be cushioned with a small folded towel, arms should be bent loosely at sides.

• The masseur needs some oil to facilitate the massage – almond oil is usual for the 'base oil', which can be mixed with a few drops of a relaxing essential oil, such as clary sage or lavender. The oil should be at body temperature and just enough to lubricate the skin should be used.

Basic massage techniques

If someone is going to massage you, they need to understand the simple techniques of stroking, kneading, knuckling, pressure and pummelling. All are based on common sense.

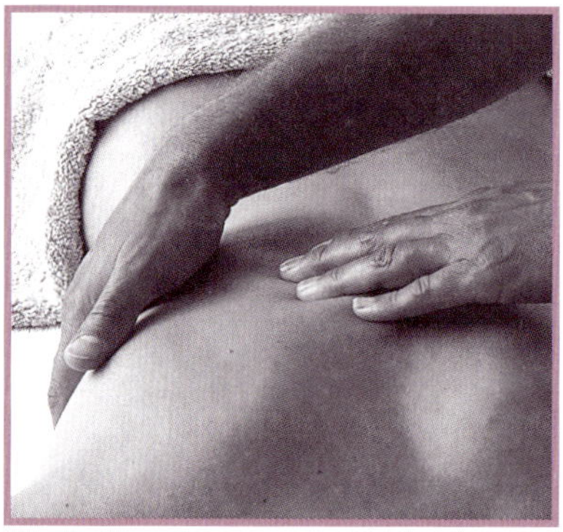

STROKING: Light strokes using fingers of both hands to smooth and soothe the skin. Speed and pressure can be varied but this is not a heavy-pressure technique.

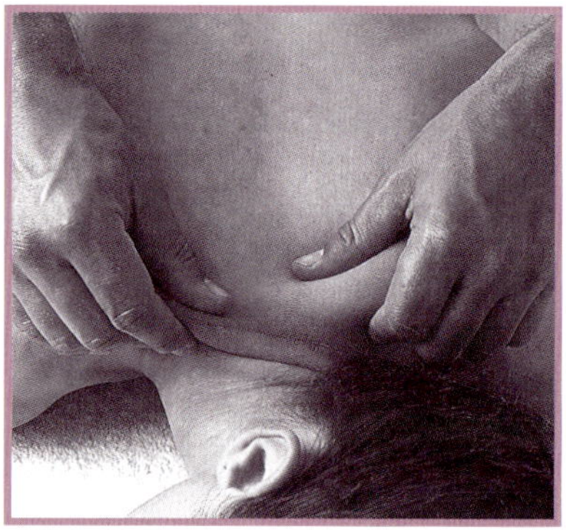

KNEADING: Gathering flesh between the thumb and fingers and kneading, pulling, squeezing, perhaps stretching with the other hand. Light to moderate pressure, used on the fleshier areas of the body.

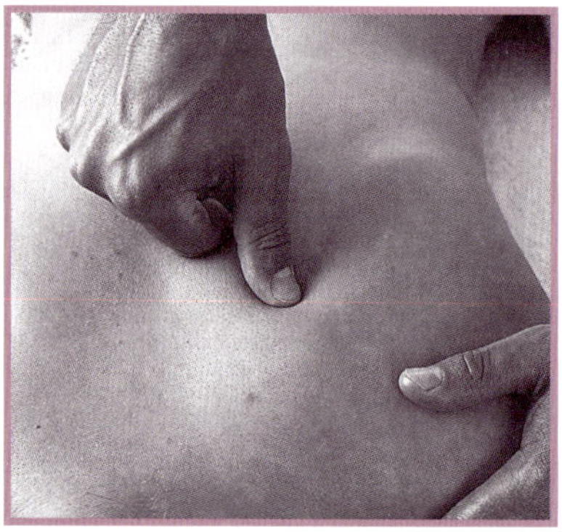

KNUCKLING: Lightly fisted hand (usually right hand) uses moderate or deeper pressure to massage tense areas. Especially useful for the feet and palms. Elbows and feet can also be used to increase pressure if the masseur's hands are weak or tired.

• The masseur needs to have warm hands, short nails, no rings, and to be in a good and giving mood. Try to keep at least one hand on the body at all times during a massage.

• Do not massage injured areas, varicose veins or breasts. The recipient must say if the massage is truly painful at any stage, in which case a lighter or different stroke should be tried; it is probably wiser to move to another area of the body. As a general rule, firm massage strokes should work towards the heart.

• Do not massage anyone who has a serious medical condition without the consent of their physician. Do not use essential oils on a pregnant woman without prior professional consultation.

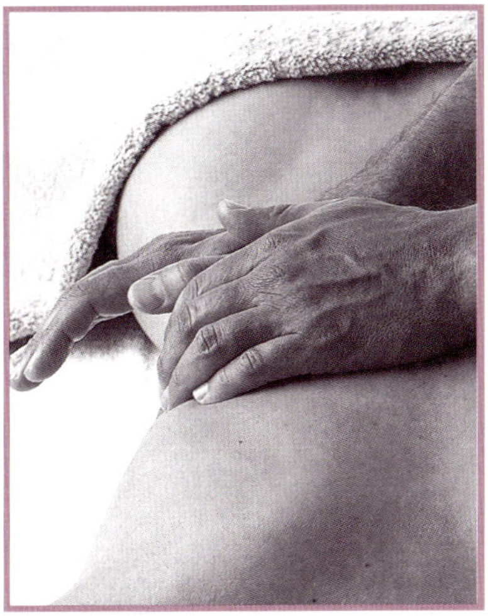

PRESSURE: Using the thumb, fingers or even elbow or heel to press firmly into a muscle where knots of tension, stiffness or pain lie. Will release tension and increase blood flow to the area. Referred pain may be felt elsewhere in the body. Pressure is generally held until the pain melts away, or released and repeated if the spot is very sore. You can also use small circular movements, keeping the pressure fairly even. Most useful for shoulders and neck and feet. 'Good pain', but not true 'painful pain', should be felt. Varicose veins and broken skin should be avoided.

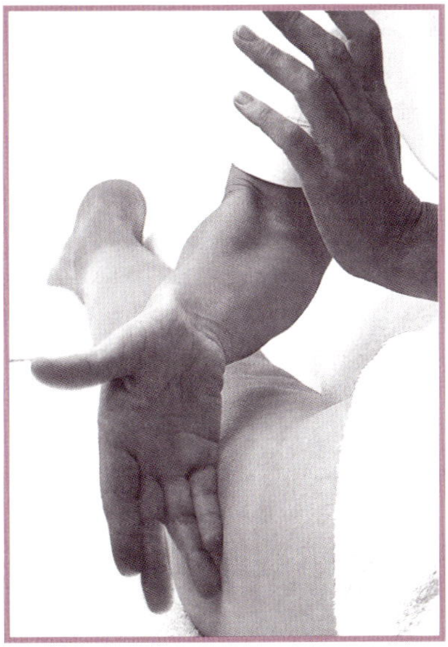

PUMMELLING: The outside edge of both hands is used to pummel the larger areas of the body with a good covering of flesh. Not to be used on delicate or thinly fleshed areas. Stimulates circulation.

Position yourself comfortably to one side of recipient before you begin the massage.

1 Start with long light strokes up and down either side of the spine, then large circles, left hand anticlockwise, right hand clockwise on either side of the back. Stroke from either side of base of neck out across tops of shoulders, using moderate pressure with the palms of the hands. Stroke the length of the outer left arm from hand to shoulder; repeat with right arm. Now stroke down either side of the body towards the waist, fingers together, thumbs apart. Continue down to the buttocks and then each leg in turn and back again more firmly, and repeat several times, gradually increasing the pressure around the thighs, calves and buttocks, and kneading lightly in the fleshier areas as described above.

2 Move the hands back up the body, stroking more firmly, and knead the fleshy areas around shoulders and waist, paying particular attention to knots of tension in the lower neck area. If kneading is too painful at first, apply moderate pressure with the forefingers to release tension before kneading again or going on to the next stage.

3 Work further on the knots that you have found, with some pressure work (see above). Moderate or increase the pressure according to how the recipient feels.

4 A short period of pummelling (see page 27) on the knotted fleshy areas can follow if you like.

5 Now stroke smoothly down to the left foot. Cradling it in your left hand, knuckle the sole as described on page 26 with the right hand and then repeat with the other foot. Massage each toe in turn, using forefinger and thumb, and then return up the body, stroking lightly until you reach the neck. Cover the recipient and ask them to rest for as long as they like.

If shorter periods of time are available, here are some suggestions for quick but effective massages:

- Scalp and neck massage using circular pressure with thumbs and forefingers.
- Neck and shoulder massage, combining pressure and kneading.
- Face massage (for technique, see facial massage panel, page 30).
- Foot massage (for technique, see self-massage for the feet, page 32).
- Abdominal massage, using light stroking, followed by light circular pressure with the palm of each hand. It is surprising how knotted up the abdominal area can get when a person is under stress.

Massage help

Various electric hand-held massagers are available ranging from £20 or so up to £200. The cheaper ones tend to deliver a very light massage and some are very noisy. In general you get what you pay for.
If you are buying, look for one with a long handle and plenty of weight in the head so you can do your own back easily.

Other types of massage equipment include expensive table-type mattresses that you lie on, cushions that you place behind your back, and wooden roller-ball boards for foot massage.

There are several good books on massage technique. If you have a partner to massage you regularly it might well be worth investing in one.

OTHER RELATED THERAPIES
Shiatsu, reflexology, and lymphatic drainage massage are dealt with elsewhere in the book. See the index.

Self-massage

Bear in mind all the rules of massage laid out earlier on pages 26–8. Not all areas of the body are actually suitable for self-massage, but you can target many of the areas that are most likely to be carrying tension. If you have time, do all six of the areas outlined below, which should take 12–18 minutes. If not, pick just one, two or three – your own instincts should help you decide which areas are actually most needy. About 2–3 minutes is the minimum time you should aim to spend on each.

1 SCALP If you are tense, the skin on your scalp will not move easily on the skull underneath. Sit, as relaxedly as you can, in a low-backed chair. Starting above the forehead and using the fingers of both hands, carry out small circular pressure strokes, working slowly backwards on either side towards the top of your neck, and then outwards around behind your ears and up and out to the temples.

2 FACE AND EYES This is good for relieving eye strain and headache. You must always be very gentle on your face, especially in the area around the eyes, using only very light pressure with one or more fingers, light strokes using the little finger, or very light strokes using all the fingers flat on the face as described overleaf. Use a little vitamin E oil or almond oil – avoid any of the essential oils, as these may well sting your eyes if some accidentally gets into them. It is best to do this massage while lying relaxedly on your back if you can, or otherwise sitting in a low-backed chair, or even in the bath.

Brush your hair back off your face and secure it if necessary. Warm your hands if you need to and spread a little oil on the palms.

Keep your eyes lightly shut while you massage. Starting under the jaw, use light, flat-fingered strokes to smooth the oil into the face – over the jaw, around the mouth, up the cheeks and round the temples, then across the forehead.

Now using the middle two fingers of either hand placed just above the inner eyebrows, exert light pressure on your forehead for a count of three. Move the fingers a little and repeat the process, going across each side of the forehead, then down each temple and finally across the cheekbones, until you finish with the fingers either side of your nose.

Using the little fingers of both hand, smooth upwards on each side of the nose and then up over the bridge of the nose to the forehead.

Now place the pad of each thumb on the lower side of the jawbone directly under your chin. Smoothly glide the thumbs outwards under the jaw, following the bone, and finish the move underneath the earlobe. Repeat this a few times.

Lastly, using the forefingers, find the spot just in front of each ear and below the cheekbone where if you use small circular pressure movements you will probably feel tender. Continue the movements back and up towards the ear itself.

Finish by placing the palms of both hands over your eyes and relax in the dark.

Facial massage

(See 2 above) A three-minute self-administered facial massage is very relaxing – try it while you're in the bath or lying in bed. If you're sitting, try to keep the shoulders relaxed.

1 Exert light pressure on your forehead for a count of 3 – starting at the inner brows and moving across the temples.

2 Finish your facial massage by placing the palms of both your hands over your eyes for at least 30 seconds.

3 NECK. Oil isn't essential for this massage. Remove any clothing or jewellery around the neck. Sit in a low-backed chair and relax your neck and shoulders as much as you can. Using the fingers of each hand, stroke either side of the spinal cord in the neck, lightly at first and then more firmly. Stroke up towards the skull, then down. Knead the same area lightly, then more firmly. Use the forefingers to apply light – then firmer – pressure up and down the same area. To reach the place where your neck joins your shoulders you will need to raise your elbows upwards and backwards. Finish the neck massage by using your thumb pads to pressure-circle the area where the neck joins the skull.

4 SHOULDERS. Starting position as in Neck self-massage. Bring the right hand across your body and rest it on the top of your left shoulder. With all the finger pads, exert pressure, moving the fingers slowly from the back of the shoulder to the front. This way you can exert more pressure than if you go from front to back. If you find a tender spot, use constant pressure until it is relieved. Repeat to the other side with the left hand.

5 ABDOMEN. You need to be undressed and lying down for this one. Apply a little oil, as per the instructions on page 26, to the stomach area – from underneath the breastbone to the top of the

Neck and shoulder massage

(See 3 & 4 above) For each of the exercises below, sit with good posture in a supportive chair and try to relax your neck and shoulders as much as you can.

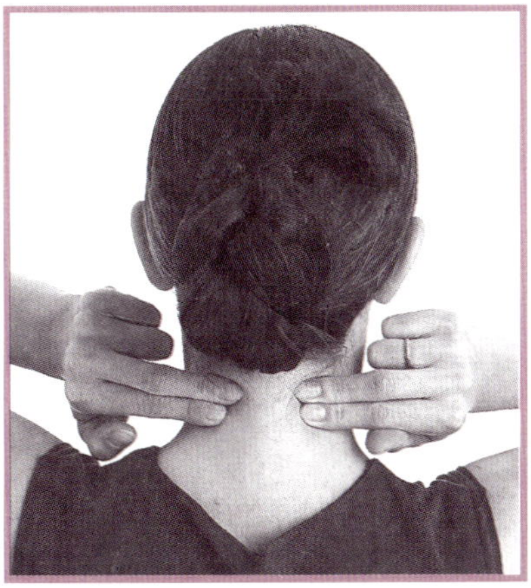

1 Using the fingers of each hand, stroke either side of the neck, lightly at first and then beginning to knead more firmly.

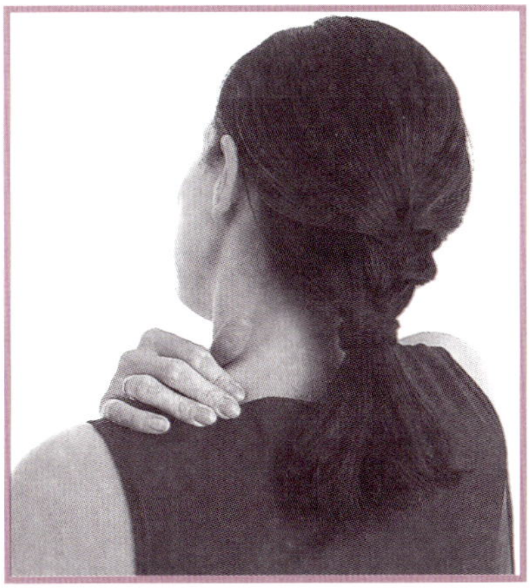

2 Bring the right hand across your body and exert pressure with all finger pads. Repeat to the other side with left hand.

pubic bone – and use light stroking to massage the whole area, starting at the top and working down. Breathe calmly and deeply as you massage. Try to find the knots in your stomach and work on them with light circular pressure, using all the fingertips of each hand.

6 FEET. Sit with bare feet, preferably with no clothing on the legs, in a large and low comfortable chair. Bend the right knee outwards and place your right foot on top of your left thigh, low down towards the left knee so that you can see the sole of your right foot. Place the fingers of the left hand underneath the foot near the toes and the fingers of right hand just below the front of the ankle, so that both thumbs are free. Now begin massaging the sole, using pressure applied with each thumb pad for a few seconds at a time, repeating the pressure when you find a particularly tender or sore area. Cover the whole of the sole and instep methodically. Then, with the left thumb and fingers, massage each toe in turn, then stroke the top of the foot with the fingers of the left hand, increasing the pressure if you like.

Repeat the whole procedure with the left foot on your right thigh.

Breathing and posture for relaxation

Incorrect breathing technique has a direct and chronic effect upon the way you feel, both physically and mentally. Correct breathing can increase energy and mental alertness, as discussed later in this Step and in Step 2. However, correct breathing can also relax you and calm you down, slowing your brainwaves to the quiet condition known as the alpha state.

When we're under stress, frightened, tense or suffering from a variety of other negative emotions, our breathing involuntarily becomes quicker and more shallow (we may even stop breathing altogether for a while). This adversely affects the balance of oxygen and carbon dioxide in the blood and result in feelings of anxiety, panic, light-headedness and other symptoms associated with stress.

If you have a high-stress lifestyle, you may begin to breathe this way most of the time, even when not particularly stressed out, as a matter of habit. Ironically this will mean you soon do feel stressed, creating a vicious circle of tension/poor breathing/more tension.

However, by making a point of altering the way we breathe to mimic the way we do it when relaxed – slowing the breathing rate down, breathing from the diaphragm and the stomach rather than the upper chest – we can kid our brains and bodies that we are relaxed, until eventually we are. Good breathing is so vital to the relaxation process that you need to practise on a daily basis in order to gain most benefit from the other parts of this Step.

You also need to look at your posture, as poor body alignment – particularly the hunched shoulders that often accompany chronic stress – can hamper good breathing and, in addition, can increase muscle tension. This creates another vicious circle: poor posture/ poor breathing/increased feelings of anxiety/increased muscle tension/poorer posture.

Longer-term, poor breathing and poor posture can easily result in the muscles of the diaphragm being too stiff and tense to expand (stretch) properly when you do try to breathe deeply, so you will need to do regular breathing, postural and stretching work for some time before everything is back to how nature intended.

The exercises on this page will help you to breathe, sit and stand properly – and, therefore, relax. The stretches and yoga-based exercises on the following pages will also help:

Breathing exercise 1 – normal breathing

Sit as relaxedly as you can, shoulders down, arms loose at your sides.

- Think about how you're breathing now. Is it shallow? Is it quick?
- Take a big sighing breath through the nose. You may be surprised how much of a relief it is to breathe deeply.
- On the same breath, breathe into the chest, diaphragm and then stomach, to a count of 5. Watch each area expanding as you do so.
- Breathe out through the mouth from the stomach, diaphragm and chest to a count of 5.

Try to breathe this way when at rest – get into the habit of checking your breathing many times during the day. You'll probably find that your diaphragm doesn't expand as much as it should to start with, for the reasons outlined above. Gradually, as you continue to breathe more deeply, the whole process will become second nature.

When working the body, e.g. during exercise, keep the stomach muscles strong and just breathe into the diaphragm.

Breathing exercise 2 – deep relax

Lie on your back on a mat or firm bed. Shut your eyes. Place your hands on either side of the lower ribcage. Take a big breath through the nose to a count of 4, feeling your hands rise up as you inhale. Breathe out to a count of 6, using your fingers to press gently but firmly into the diaphragm (at base of ribcage), helping expel all the air from your lungs. Exhaling correctly is as important as inhaling correctly. Repeat 10 times, working up to 20 times over a few days.

Posture watching

Good posture comes from a strong base – strong stomach and lower back muscles – with a well-balanced skeleton on which the muscles can sit – and work – in harmony, neither overworked (and therefore perhaps over-bulky or with lactic acid build-up) or underworked (and, therefore, perhaps over-lengthened or too tight). Poor posture can create a great deal of musculo-skeletal tension. You can't be relaxed and happy – or, indeed, energetic – if you have an aching body permanently placed under the stress of imbalance.

Here is one example of how poor posture affects your muscles and your life.

If you sit in an easy chair with your tailbone too far forward, that means your spine is sloped backwards and the muscles at the top of your back on the shoulders have to work all the time you stay in this position to keep your head up. These muscles build up tension and lactic acid and then you wonder why you have a sore neck and shoulders! Correct posture as you sit would mean that your head is balanced naturally on your neck and those poor muscles only have to do very light work to keep the head stabilized. Result – no problem. Correct posture in this instance will also mean that your ribcage can expand more easily when you breathe.

A second example is that of the person who slumps over an office desk all day with rounded shoulders. Is that you? The result will again be neck tension as the same muscles mentioned above have to work too hard to keep the head erect. You are also lengthening (stretching) the muscles of the lower and outer shoulders, meaning that when you do decide to start sitting correctly again your shoulders will be weak and you will need to do strength exercise to correct the problem.

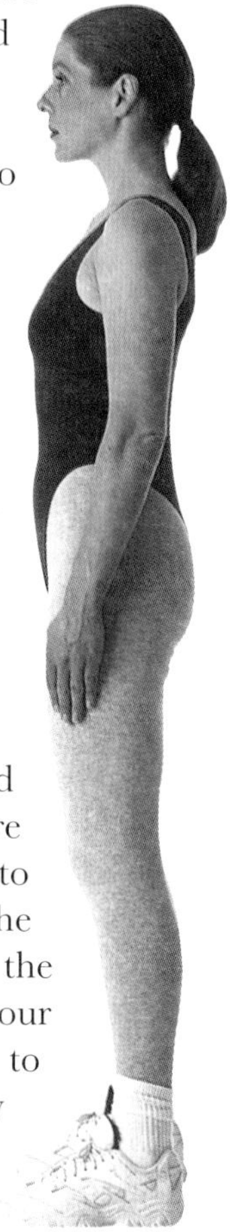

Lastly you are shortening (tightening) the muscles across the chest which again hampers breathing and means that you may need to do stretching exercise on the chest muscles in order to regain good posture. Instead, sitting with a strong lower back, strong stomach and relaxed shoulders, with any work at a correct height so that you can carry it out without slumping, will result in your body coping much better with sedentary work, and your feeling much less tense and tired at the end of the day.

Look at the illustrations here and try to sit and stand like this throughout the day. If you've had poor posture for years, the correct positions may feel unnatural to you. Don't be put off – simply work at the postures, the stretching exercises on the following pages and, later, the Strength Programme in Step 2, and you will find your body in much better alignment within weeks. Try to think about your posture many times during the day and keep correcting it until the right way becomes natural to you.

Standing

Stand with your pelvis centred correctly (not tilted forward as many people do, with its attendant protruding stomach), using your stomach muscles to maintain equilibrium and keeping your knees relaxed, not locked. Your lower back will now have a gentle, but not exaggerated, curve. From this position, straighten up your central and upper spine so your shoulders aren't slumped forward and your head isn't poking forward or down. Shoulders should be held relaxed but down (shrug them a few times to see how 'up' and 'tight' they are and to loosen them). Neck and head should sit comfortably balanced on your spine, which will mean you needn't create muscle tension in that area to support the head/neck. Your chest will now be 'open' and ribcage free to expand properly during breathing (remember that tight chest muscles may take a while to loosen, as explained opposite).

Check your posture (illustrated opposite) many times a day. Walk with the same posture.

Sitting

Try to ensure chairs used regularly offer adequate support to the lower back and help good posture. Sit with your tailbone at the back of the seat, pelvis tilted slightly to the back so the stomach naturally pulls in towards your spine, feet flat on the floor. Keep mid and lower back strong to avoid slumping; shoulders relaxed and down, head balanced softly on your neck which should, in turn, sit lightly on the shoulders.

Ensure whatever you are working on, is a suitable distance away and at the correct height so you can maintain this position. Take short rests every hour, perhaps walking around the room or doing one or two sitting stretches, or the tense-and-release exercise described on page 38. Concentrate on relaxing shoulders and neck.

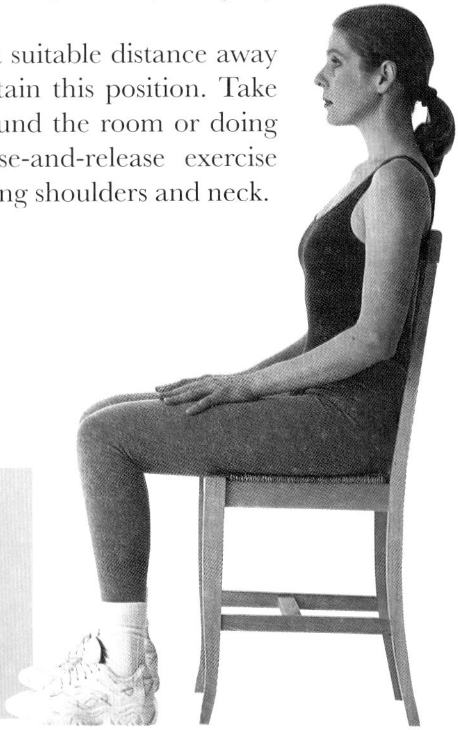

Tip

You may like to try either the Alexander Technique or Pilates, both of which achieve excellent results in improving posture and breathing. Books on the subjects are available but initially, at least, personal training is preferable. See the Appendix.

Stretching and deep relaxation

The stretches on this page will help your muscles to relax, help improve your posture and help focus your mind too. They will also prepare your body for the slightly harder poses involved in yoga which you may also want to try (see pages 38–41).

Use them when your body is warm at any time of the day. Do your stretches wearing comfortable clothes, in a warm room, on a mat and while breathing correctly – slowly and deeply. Go into the stretch as you exhale. As you hold the stretch, don't forget to breathe. Hold each stretch for a count of 10, relax then repeat – you will find you have 'relaxed into the stretch' and can stretch a bit further. Gradually increase the length of time you stretch, up to a minute or more.

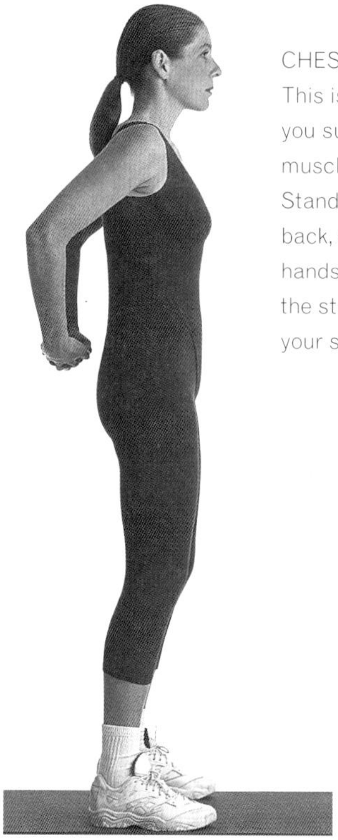

CHEST STRETCH

This is important if your breathing is tight and you suffer from round shoulders and tight chest muscles.

Stand with your hands clasped behind your back, shoulders down and relaxed. Bring the hands out away from the back until you feel the stretch across your chest and the front of your shoulders.

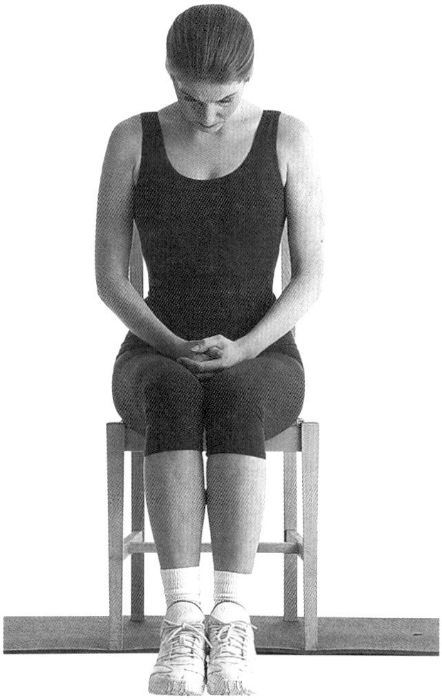

SPINAL STRETCH 1

This easy version is for those who are particularly stiff and inflexible.

Sit on a chair, breathe out and drop your head, neck and spine forward, feeling the stretch along the spine. Use your hands gently to stretch out the neck if you like.

Upper shoulder and chest stretch

This is a version of the yoga Warrior pose – you will probably need a small towel or face flannel if you are very inflexible.

Kneel or sit on a stool with your spine in a straight but relaxed posture, shoulders relaxed. Bring the left hand up behind your back, palm outwards. Bring the right arm over your right shoulder and down, palm inwards. Try to clasp both hands together (use the towel or flannel if you can't, one end in each hand). Hold and repeat to the other side.

SPINAL STRETCH 2

This harder version is for intermediates, giving a bigger stretch to the spine and increasing blood flow to the brain; it also stretches chest and shoulders. Avoid this exercise if you have knee trouble.

Kneel with the buttocks on your heels as shown (right), and bring the body forward over your thighs, with the back of the neck elongated to tuck the head into the knees. Rest the arms to either side of legs, with palms upwards as shown. Breathe slowly.

A slightly easier version (below) is to rest with the arms stretched out in front of you and the palms on the floor.

LONG BODY STRETCH

For whole body relaxation, breathing and elongation: Lie on your back on the floor with your arms above your head (on the floor), toes pointing. Tilt pelvis up slightly to close the gap between the lower back and floor a little. If you are very inflexible, you may not be able to touch the floor with your hands while keeping the bottom, upper back and feet on floor – but if you do this stretch every day you soon will. Breathe slowly and deeply, and relax into the posture – you will feel your stomach muscles, diaphragm and shoulders stretching. Bring your chin down to close the gap between neck and floor slightly. When you're completely relaxed into the stretch, hold up to 2 minutes.

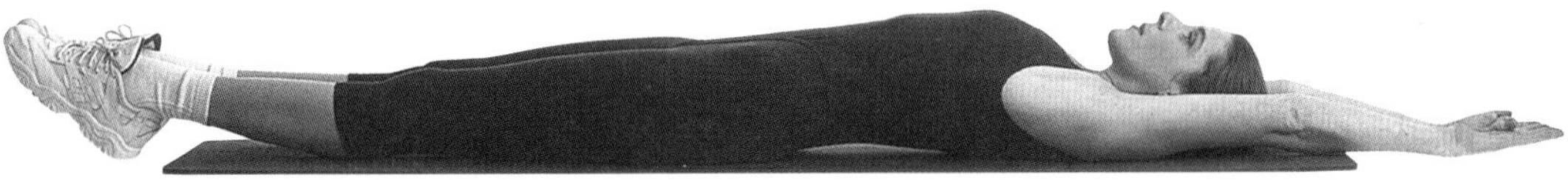

Deep relaxation – the 'tense and relax' technique

For this you need somewhere quiet and comfortable to lie down. The full process will take several minutes. Try it in the morning to help you relax and focus on the day; try it before bed to help you sleep. Practised daily, it will help you relax long-term.

Lie on your back and do the deep relax breathing exercise as on page 33. Now, with the eyes shut, focus on each part of your body in turn, first tensing that part as much as you can and then relaxing it as much as you can. As you tense each part, breathe in; as you relax, breathe out. So you tense for 5, relax for 5.

Start with your toes. Bunch them up tight; breathing in. Relax them, breathing out. Now on to the feet, and so on through calves, thighs, hips, stomach, diaphragm, fingers, hands, forearms, upper arms, lower back, upper back, shoulders, neck and head. By the time you finish you should be completely relaxed and 'sinking into the bed'. Lie there for a few minutes, breathing correctly, eyes closed. If you have time, lie and let your mind drift and see where it goes. This may be a good time for you to unlock deep-seated emotions, helping the mind to detox. Finish by slowly rolling on to your side and getting up.

If you haven't time for the full-body 'tense and relax', concentrate just on the parts that are holding the most tension – often the neck, shoulders, hands and feet.

Yoga and meditation

Yoga is well known for its benefits in aiding deep mental and physical relaxation. With its origins in India about 5,000 years ago, the yoga most often practised in the West is Hatha Yoga, which basically concentrates on postures (*asanas*), which stretch and re-align the body, breathing (*pranayama*), which relaxes and centres the mind and body, and can also include meditation (*dhyana*), which calms and focuses, to produce a completely well-balanced body and a refreshed mind.

Many people concentrate just on the postures and breathing, which alone will bring much benefit in relaxing. If your muscles are very tensed up, the more difficult poses will be harder to do correctly at first. However, if you do pre-stretching (see previous pages) and practise the simpler yoga postures at least once a day, your body will rapidly become more supple and the muscles will relax into the poses. Breathing correctly is an important part of yoga and the deep breathing technique on page 33 is suitable for beginners' yoga.

The Half Lotus pose and Sun Salutation sequence shown here are but a taster of the huge subject that is yoga. For some more information on books, classes, etc., see the Appendix.

The Sun Salutation sequence

This is a flowing sequence of movements (pictured overleaf) with each pose held for just a few seconds – unlike *asanas* or postures, which are usually done separately and held for 30 seconds or more. Traditionally it is carried out at dawn; you may prefer to do it at whatever time you wake, or at any time of day as long as you haven't eaten recently. It helps to oxygenate the body, improves circulation, relieves tension and releases energy – as well as improving flexibility and body tone tremendously.

Just go as far as you can into each movement without strain or pain. If you do the salutation about 4 or 5 times a week, gradually working up to 10 sequences every day, your body and your well-being will quickly show improvement. The correct breathing is, as usual, important.

The Half Lotus position

The Lotus is the position generally used for meditation as it is relaxing and encourages breath control and concentration. The full Lotus is too hard for most beginners. This Half Lotus is easier.

Sit on the floor with the legs relaxed to the front, and bend the right leg so that the right foot comes in near the left thigh. Let your right knee fall outward towards the floor. Now bend the left knee and bring the left foot under the right leg, letting the left knee drop to the floor. An alternative position for the left foot is to sit it on top of the right leg near your groin – do whichever feels more comfortable for you. Now rest your hands on your knees, with the palms facing upwards, straighten your spine and relax.

Meditation – what is it?

The postures and deep breathing of yoga are often combined with meditation and, perhaps, with chanting. Meditation produces deep relaxation and inner peace by calming the mind and focusing it. The brain's alpha waves increase (beyond those induced by sleep) and both pulse rate and breathing rate slow down. Long-term, meditation can greatly reduce high blood pressure, stress, anxiety, fatigue and insomnia.

A simple form of meditation is simply to sit in the Half Lotus position (though this isn't obligatory and if you have knee problems you may prefer just to sit in any relaxed position), close your eyes and concentrate on listening to your breathing. If outside thoughts come into your mind, send them away. Picture them floating away on a cloud or down a stream. Another aid to meditation is to repeat a word or phrase over and over, either silently or out loud. This is your 'mantra'. Pick a word or phrase that you like but which doesn't excite you, such as 'peace' or 'life', or use the traditional Hindu mantra 'Om'.

The Sun Salutation Sequence shown here is a flowing sequence of movements – for more information, see page 39.

1 Stand with feet slightly apart and hands in the prayer position as shown. Breathe deeply and slowly a few times.

2 INHALE as you raise your arms above your head, gently bending your spine back from the waist, if able, and pushing your pelvis forward.

3 EXHALE as you smoothly bend forward, so that your head touches your knees (if you can) and your hands grasp the ankles (bending the knees will help).

4 INHALE and move your right leg back in a big step so that your right knee is slightly bent and your toes supporting your right leg. The left foot remains where it was and the palms are placed on the floor either side of the left leg. Look upwards.

5 HOLD THE BREATH and now bring the left leg back to join the right leg. Straighten the knees and arms so that you are in a semi push-up position.

6 EXHALE while lowering the body to the floor via the knees then the forehead, chest and pelvis.

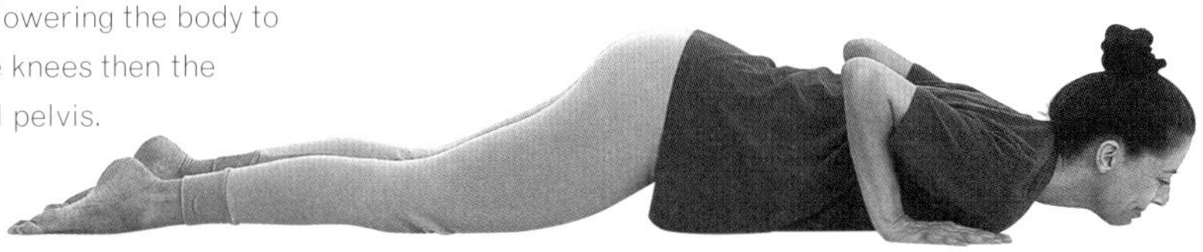

7 INHALE and push the upper body up until the arms are straight and the back is arched into the Cobra position. Look up at the ceiling (if you can).

8 EXHALE and push your body weight on to your hands, bringing the buttocks up so the body is in an inverted 'V' shape, with your feet flat on floor, the back and arms long, and head tucked in between your arms.

9 INHALE and bring the right leg forward, so that your body is in the same position as step 4, but mirrored.

10 EXHALE and bring your left leg forward, then straighten your legs and drop the torso into same position as in step 3.

11 INHALE and raise the torso and arms into the same position as step 2.

12 EXHALE and drop your arms to the sides, relaxing your posture. Breathe slowly for a few seconds and repeat the Sun Salutation Sequence from 1 to 10 times. Rest for a few minutes before continuing with your day.

Really Relax

Relaxation comes in many forms – and too often, when life is busy and we are stressed out, we tend to ignore the simple things that can help us calm down and release emotion. Use some or all of the ideas outlined on these pages, along with the methods set out on the previous pages.

Music and dancing

For thousands of years, humans have understood the power of music to calm and relax – as well as to incite every other emotion that we possess. Soothing music can be used to calm you down after a busy day or an argument; sad music can be used to help you release bottled-up grief or long-buried memories. If you're stressed out, don't discount putting on some disco music and dancing as hard as you can until you collapse – exhausted but relaxed.

Also, don't forget to use suitable music to help you with breathing exercises or stretching, or to help bring out emotions while you have a massage.

Relaxation audio aids

There are many CDs and tapes available which will calm and relax you – from the sounds of ocean waves to birdsong or Hindu chants. There are also self-help tapes presented by various therapists to teach you to relax. See what is available and pick something that appeals to you.

Aromatherapy

The aromas of various essential plant oils can affect your mood in a variety of ways – some stimulate, others refresh, others calm and relax.

The most obvious use of aromatherapy oils is to aid massage. A few drops of the chosen oil are mixed with a 'base oil', such as almond oil, and this will not only feel good on the skin but also penetrate the pores of the skin, and you will breathe the aroma in as it evaporates. Other uses of the oils include putting a few drops in the bath water or on a handkerchief, or spraying around your bedroom or sitting room.

Aromatherapy is fairly well researched and really does work. Small phials of the oils can be bought from most chemists, as can the base oil. They should be stored in cool, dark conditions and not kept for years – the base oil can become oxidized and the essential oils lose their potency.

Calming essential oils include clary sage, lavender, ylang-ylang, bergamot and sandalwood. For more information on aromatherapy, see the Appendix.

Getting away from it all

If you can afford the time or money, how about spending a few days – or more – on complete relaxation and pampering? For more information on all of these ideas, see the Appendix.

A RETREAT
A place to really switch off, or to spend some time on introspection if you prefer. There are retreats all over the UK and Europe, offering varying degrees of luxury/privacy.

A HEALTH FARM
Usually more expensive and more sociable than a retreat, but with a wide range of treatments that should actively help the relaxation process.

A YOGA WEEKEND
Improve your yoga technique while you calm down and unwind. This is a low-cost alternative, for those who really don't mind sharing.

Water therapy

This can be as simple as a warm bath taken when you most need it, with no feeling that you have to rush to get out of the water. The heat of the water relaxes the muscles fairly quickly and the calming process can be enhanced if you light a few scented candles in the bathroom and turn out the electric light, and/or add a soothing perfumed oil to the water. You can also use a brush or mitt to rub your muscles and this is a good opportunity to do some deep breathing exercises.

Laughter

Research shows that regular laughter can reduce blood pressure, as well as help calm the nerves and increase physical and mental relaxation. If there aren't many opportunities in your normal daily life to laugh out loud, consider hiring videos of your favourite comedians or check out the humorous novels available at your local library.

Diet

The type of food you eat can have an effect on how calm you feel. Carbohydrates (bread, potatoes, pasta, rice, cereals) calm you down and so do calcium-rich foods such as milk and cheese. Therefore, a cheese sandwich may be the answer in a crisis.

Alcohol is NOT the answer, however. Although one or two drinks may relax the nerves, alcohol is a depressant and long-term will neither help you to relax NOR increase energy.

1

Tiredness is the great thief of vitality. You can't have optimum energy if both brain and body are weighed down with fatigue and lassitude. Learn here how to manage sleep, beat fatigue and stop feeling 'tired all the time'.

sleep truths

adequate sleep is vital to mind, body, spirit and energy

Here we look at the relationship between sleep, rest, tiredness and energy – and discover that things are not always as they seem...

Are you tired all the time? Do you worry that you don't get enough rest? We all get tired sometimes; indeed 'good tiredness' – the sort of tiredness that comes from a day well spent and properly balanced – is what you need if you are to have a good night's sleep and re-energize yourself for the next day. Tiredness is also the natural way the body and brain have of telling you they need sleep. Occasional overtiredness probably simply means you have been doing too much.

However, if you have 'bad tiredness', when you're mentally and/or physically exhausted but also stressed out, it is all too easy to be so wound up that you can't relax and can't sleep. Another type of 'bad tiredness' is what I call the Sloth Syndrome – feeling almost permanently lethargic and dull despite doing little physically or mentally, and spending many hours in bed.

We examine all these kinds of tiredness and see how to replace the bad with the good, so that you get enough energizing sleep without falling into the 'tiredness traps'.

What is adequate rest?

We can't be truly energetic without enough rest and sleep, because it is during this time that the body and mind regenerate and repair themselves. But what IS adequate rest? This varies quite considerably from person to person but, generally, rest needs to be of a good quality, and the quantity needs to be just right.

Quality

The quality of rest and sleep is probably more important than the quantity. It is also all too often the quality of sleep that goes when we are under negative stress, particularly mental or emotional stress. Quality sleep contains adequate REM sleep – light, dream sleep, when our brains appear to 'file' our wakeful goings-on and thoughts – and adequate deep, non-REM sleep, when our bodies repair themselves, and growth and sex hormones are released. Both types of sleep are necessary for you to wake feeling refreshed...

All the guidelines given so far in this Step will aid good sleep. Any relaxation therapies that you can carry out during the evening should help – massage, deep breathing, stretching, yoga and the other self-calming techniques will help to calm the brain and relax the body. Here, though, are some more specific ideas for helping you to achieve a good night's rest.

If you're not sleeping well it may simply be a case of not being tired enough. If you don't get enough daily physical exercise you may sleep badly, as you may if there isn't enough balance in your life. The three following Steps in the book will help you to include more exercise in your life and get it in better balance, but start now by taking a daily walk. Try going to bed a little later for a week too and see if that makes a difference. Also pay attention to your own 'body clock' (see page 46).

Middle-of-the-night waking is one of the clearest indications that you're not going to get a good night's sleep. This may be caused by too much alcohol the previous evening, causing low blood sugar several hours into sleep, or by anxiety and stress – this could be your problem if you wake with a start, stomach churning, mind sharp, thinking about your life's problems. To overcome this you need to work on these problems – Steps 3 and 4 will help – while following all the other tips here to ensure that at least you are physically tired in the 'good' way. Try not to go to bed with work worries unresolved; writing a 'to do' list for tomorrow, at the end of every working day, may help you relax. For deep-rooted anxieties or life crises, you may want to consider counselling – see the Appendix.

To help break this kind of pattern, a short course of herbal sleeping tablets (those based on valerian are very good) will help without being addictive. Prescription sleeping pills are not a good idea as they suppress REM (dreaming) sleep, which is essential for good health. The body also gets used to them if used too often, so that they become less effective, and if you stop taking them sleep may be even harder to find.

Ensure a comfortable bed and bedroom – a mattress that suits you, pillows that suit you, adequate bedding which isn't too heavy. Ideal air temperature is cool but not freezing – never leave central heating on overnight in the bedroom. Turn the heating off when you put the light out – you won't need it. And I'd always have a window open in the bedroom, otherwise you will end the night feeling sluggish and stuffy and not want to get up at all

Think about your food and drink intake in the evenings. If you're hungry at bedtime you're unlikely to get a good night's sleep as your blood sugar levels will be low. If you've had a blow-out you may be kept awake with indigestion. A moderate evening meal about 3 hours before bedtime is ideal. Calcium-rich foods such as milk or yoghurt are good, as calcium is known as 'nature's tranquillizer'. Carbohydrate-rich foods, such as bread or rice, will help you to sleep because they increase the production of the mood-enhancing chemical serotonin in the brain. Protein foods rich in the amino acid tryptophan can also induce production of serotonin. A mug of hot milk before bedtime may, therefore, be the perfect answer as it contains both tryptophan and calcium in excellent quantities, and lactose, a milk sugar (which is a carbohydrate).

Quantity

The average amount of sleep that adults need every night is 7–8 hours, assuming a normal pattern of restful and deep sleep, but some people get by happily on 6 hours or even less, while others thrive on 9. As long as you are going to bed, sleeping through the night and waking refreshed and energized, then you are getting enough sleep. Here are three tips about the length of time you are asleep.

1 Try not to have a huge variation in the time you go to sleep/get up all the time. For example, you may go to bed at 11 p.m. and get up at 7 a.m. during the working week, but then go to bed at 2 a.m. and lie in until lunchtime at weekends. This isn't ideal – even if you're later some nights, it is best to get up at a reasonable hour. For reliable sleep, the body needs to be given fairly regular hours – disturb the body clock too much and, even if you don't now, in later years you may have a problem.

2 If you habitually have to get up to an alarm clock and when it goes off you are always in a deep sleep, try going to bed a bit earlier! It is best to be at the 'nearly awake' stage when the alarm goes off – meaning you've had adequate sleep.

3 If your typical night's sleep is punctured by long hours awake, so that when it is time to get up you feel exhausted, don't be tempted to stay in bed – get up anyway and carry on through the day, using all the tips here, and hopefully tomorrow night's sleep will be better. This can take some time to work through, so don't expect instant results. However, I know from my own experience the truth of this advice – I suffered from fitful sleep and hours spent awake (often from 3 to 5 a.m.), only to drop into sleep at 6 a.m. or so, then finding myself in a deep sleep when it was time to get up at 7.30.

For years I would stay in bed until I felt okay, getting up around 9. Then I began setting the alarm for 7 and getting up. I realized even on the very first day that I didn't feel too bad – I didn't die of exhaustion during the day – and within a week of this regime I was sleeping through the night, at least most nights. I now have more time and my life is altogether better, just through a simple trick that took years to discover.

Lastly, on the subject of quantity of sleep, don't think that just because adequate sleep is necessary and ideal, even more must be better. That is the worst way to go. Too much sleep (or, at least too much lying in bed half-dozing) is probably worse than too little sleep when it comes to finding your optimum energy level, as we will discuss in the following pages.

Tired all the time

It is estimated that around 5 million people in the UK alone suffer from what has become known as the TATT (tired all the time) syndrome, what I call the Sloth Syndrome, when no matter how many hours you may spend in bed or what you do, you feel blanketed by weariness, lethargy, weakness, fatigue – the total opposite of energy ... about as low as you can go. Result – life slipping by; you doing little or nothing.

I don't believe there is just one cause of this, or one degree of it, but even in a mild form it needs to be addressed and cured. It is 'bad tiredness' at its worst and some people report its duration in years rather than weeks or months.

The first thing to check out, if you feel you suffer from the Sloth Syndrome, is your health. Many physical illnesses and health problems – from 'flu or under-active thyroid to cancer or diabetes – can cause undue fatigue, so you really need to see a physician in order to eliminate any acute or chronic illness from the list of possible causes, and I'd urge you to do so straight away. If you're not happy, get a second opinion. This book is intended for people in basic reasonable health and I don't pretend to be able to offer advice on personal health problems other than in the most general way.

A second important cause of sloth is depression – tiredness and lethargy are two major symptoms of being depressed, often with a general feeling of mental dullness. So if you have any cause to think that you may be depressed, again see a physician, who may refer you for further help if necessary. Linked with depression are stress, dissatisfaction with your life and indeed any negative emotions, all of which can produce symptoms of extreme tiredness. It is possible that this book will help you resolve such problems on its own, but if, having completed the steps, you still feel any of these negative emotions, or if your lethargy is such that you can't be bothered to do so, I would recommend that you seek further help.

The good news is that, for many, the Sloth Syndrome may be largely a result of mismanagement of yourself and the symptoms.

As you will find out in more detail in Step 2, we all need oxygen to live, and lack of oxygen can cause you to feel tired and sluggish. If you have carried out Step 1 so far, you may already be experiencing an end to the Sloth Syndrome because the breathing, posture, stretching and yoga will all have helped you to get more oxygen running through your body and brain.

In addition, regular body massage can help by releasing 'locked-up' emotions, such as anger and resentment, and buried memories, all of which may be causing knock-on fatigue and malfunctioning. This is why many people cry during a massage – it is the release of the long-held tension.

Remember – without enough air, enough oxygen, you can't feel properly alive! Obvious, really, when you think that if the body is deprived of oxygen for a very short period – minutes – it will die. Think of not breathing fully enough, not getting in enough air, as living a kind of 'half life'. You can alter that. You may find it is a simple cure for chronic tiredness.

The rules – breathe slowly and deeply from the diaphragm or stomach, expel air as thoroughly as you inhale it. Take plenty of exercise which will encourage your lungs to breathe in more air (see Step 2) and which will long-term get your heart and lungs fitter, which will again increase the amount of air that you can breathe in to oxygenate your body. Even if you can't get really active exercise – just moving around the room or office or house, preferably near an open window, will help to shake off the Sloth Syndrome.

Get plenty of fresh, cool, outdoor air. This will help you feel much more alive and cool and fresh yourself, and is especially important if you live and/or work in centrally heated places and spend hours in cars or trains or planes. Pure fresh air contains more negative ions to energize you, whereas indoor and polluted atmospheres contain more positive ions which will de-energize you. It is important, therefore, to try to find pure places full of plants and trees and with little traffic in which to walk. If you cycle in cities, buy a good anti-pollutant mask to wear.

Keep your home and/or place of work cool and wear extra clothes if you feel chilly.

Another word about exercise – apart from the extra oxygen it gives you, it also increases your blood circulation, which again will help you to feel more alive. This is especially important if you feel dull in the brain. For more on this see Step 2.

Yet another word about exercise ... If you feel physically slothful while your brain is alert, you are probably the type of person who is cerebral, not physical – your time is spent on pursuits of the brain (say, your job is research and favourite hobbies are reading, listening to music and chess) rather than anything using the body. It is very easy over time for your body to more or less 'shut down' – you may notice weight gain, feeling the cold easily, aches and pains, and physical tiredness. These are all signs that you aren't using your body enough or paying it enough attention. The metabolic rate has slowed, the important physical processes are 'rusting up' and you aren't going to feel energized again unless you begin using your body. This may take a while but you need to get into Step 2 straight away and make a start. The upside is that when you return to giving your body some attention, your brain, too, will function better, because of the extra oxygen and increased blood flow, as discussed above.

Diet

There are several links between your diet and tiredness, most of which are discussed more fully in Step 2. If you are anaemic, for example, you will probably feel very tired, but anaemia can usually be prevented with an iron-rich diet. A diet high in refined carbohydrates, such as cakes, biscuits and desserts, will make you feel sluggish and tired. Alcohol is a depressant and causes fluctuating blood sugar levels which can leave you tired. Even not drinking enough of the right kinds of drink can make you feel tired. These are just four simple cases of how diet may affect the way you feel. The Detox Diet to be found on pages 52–4 will help to clear you and energize you; then, as you move to Step 2, you will learn more about eating for long- and short-term energy.

If you go to a Chinese practitioner with symptoms of chronic tiredness and lethargy, he or she will probably cite 'too much yin' as your problem. The Oriental qualities of yin and yang balance each other out in our bodies, so the Chinese believe. Yin qualities, such as calm, peace and relaxation, are cool; while yang qualities are the dynamic ones, such as aggression and energy. In a well-balanced person, these both appear in similar amounts. Too much yin, though, will lead to depression, fatigue and all the symptoms we've been discussing above.

The problem of too much yin can be helped with all the methods described above, including oxygenating exercise and a cool, invigorating atmosphere, and also with diet – by increasing yang foods and decreasing yin foods as described below. This theory of yin and yang foods, as practised in a macrobiotic diet, isn't quite that of either my Detox Diet, which appears at the end of this Step, and is more concerned with elimination and relaxation, or the Energy Diet, which appears in Step 2 and is a more broad-based diet for energy. If you feel you have the Sloth Syndrome, however, you may like to try some adapted macrobiotic principles to help increase your yang.

Simply:

- Exclude from your diet all sugar and alcohol.
- Eat plenty of lightly cooked yang foods, some of the most important of which are brown rice and other wholegrain cereals, bread, root vegetables, fish, and all pulses, including lentils.
- And go easy on the yin foods, which are mainly fruits, nuts, seeds, vegetable and fruit juices, and tofu.
- Animal proteins (meat, eggs and cheese) are said to be over-rich in yang but might, in that case, be useful to include in your diet in small amounts.
- All food should be organic and as simply cooked as possible.

The sleep cure that will never work

To help the body cope with illness or hasten the period of convalescence, sleep is natural and bed-rest important, and this shouldn't be discounted or the natural urge for sleep overridden. If you are ill (including diagnosed ME, chronic fatigue syndrome, which IS now a recognized illness), have specific health problems or are convalescing, DO listen to your body and take what rest you need and DON'T try to get back to full energy too soon. DO NOT discount the fact that if you feel tired, you may have been doing too much and need to rest.

If, however, your Sloth Syndrome is due to any of the other possible causes listed above – or a combination, more likely – then you may have tried to cure it by what appears to be the most obvious answer – spending more and more time in bed, trying to 'catch up' on your sleep and get enough rest, which your body appears to be craving. BUT this is one cure that will rarely, if ever, work. Too much time lying in bed, whether you are asleep, dozing or simply resting or reading, is probably just about the worst thing you can do.

As we saw earlier, enough good-quality sleep is important and, if you are ill, rest and sleep are also important. If you have TATT, however, too much time in bed will probably make you worse.

The main reason for this comes back to AIR and BLOOD: your brain and your body will both feel tired if you don't get enough oxygen, if you don't breathe properly and if your circulation is sluggish. All three are not just likely, but highly probable, if you are lying in bed, when the body and brain systems naturally slow or shut down.

Also, the longer you lie in bed during the day (or outside normal sleep hours) the less likely it is that you really will get a 'good night's sleep' and so you promote yet another vicious circle in which you arrive at normal getting-up time feeling like you need more sleep still, so you lie in bed and the circle begins again. Good sleep may indeed help you, but it is quality you want (as described on the previous pages), not extra hours.

Another reason is that the longer you spend in physical inactivity, the weaker your body gets. The muscles begin to waste away, bone strength diminishes and you feel like a convalescent, even if you weren't one at the beginning of your tiredness.

Medical research published in one of the UK's most respected medical science publications showed that the majority of people with long-term ME achieved significant improvements in their energy levels when they began regular (albeit gentle) exercise rather than just resting. Imagine what it could do for the Sloth Syndrome!

So, if you are tired all the time without physical illness or diagnosed health problems, to sum up, here are the ways to improvement and eventual cure:

- Better breathing techniques, such as those already described.
- More exercise – gentle at first, such as light walking.
- More fresh air, avoiding polluted atmospheres.
- Avoid alcohol and refined carbohydrates, and follow a healthy diet, drinking plenty of water.
- Don't spend too long in bed/asleep. Begin to structure your getting-up time and, every day, try to get up a little earlier if you can't face a completely new up-time all in one go.
- Follow the programme in Step 1, including the stretch and yoga exercises and massage.
- Check out likely causes of depression and begin to build up self-awareness (see the end of this Step) before beginning work on the rest of the book.

1

Your diet has a profound influence on your energy levels. A typical Western diet will block energy by encouraging toxicity, leading to lethargy, discomfort, dehydration and general poor health.

detox diet

not until you cleanse and lighten your body through diet can you feel truly energized

The detox diet

If you've been living on a typical Western diet – high in animal protein and fats, refined produce and additives and low in fresh, natural plant foods – you will almost undoubtedly find that this is linked with a lack of energy. Along with air and water, food is essential for our survival, and we tend to live on survival rations – maybe taking in far too many calories, so we end up overweight and sluggish – as in my opinion many of us don't get all the nutrients we need in the commercial, highly refined, mass-processed items that pass for real food in our modern world. In Step 2 we will build you up with a proper high-energy diet, but first we need to detox and relax your body with this Detox Diet, which you can go on for up to a week.

Here is what the detox will do for you:

- Begin to rid your body of all the residues of junk that you may have been eating and drinking – chemicals of one kind or another. This won't happen in just a few days, as much that is toxic lies stored in body fat, but the process will get a good start here.
- Begin to give you a taste for pure and natural food, which is an ideal basis from which to move on to improved long-term eating.
- Reduce your craving for sweet and salty foods.
- Rid your body of poisons, such as alcohol, tobacco and drugs.
- Hugely increase your regular intake of invaluable antioxidants to counteract the effects of pollutants.
- Increase your intake of B vitamins to relax you.

- Increase your intake of fibre to aid the digestive process and speed elimination of toxins and waste matter, curing constipation (which encourages a heavy, lethargic feeling), as well as increasing your intake of diuretic foods (which will help fluid elimination).
- Help you lose weight and feel less sluggish physically.
- Help your brain to feel more alert and 'light'.
- Rehydrate you – lack of liquid is a common cause of fatigue.

List 1 – Not allowed

You will be taking in: NO animal foods, NO dairy produce, NO added salt, NO added sugar, NO refined produce, NO alcohol, NO highly processed foods, NO high-salt foods, NO caffeine, NO non-organic foods or drinks.

List 2 – Have plenty

Instead you'll be having: plenty of wholegrains,* especially brown rice, leafy green vegetables, broccoli, peppers, onions and garlic, raw salads especially tomatoes, celery, greens, cucumber and herbs, apples, pears and orange-fleshed melon, fresh nuts and seeds, especially walnuts, brazil nuts, sunflower and pumpkin seeds, pure water, herbal drinks, green tea.

List 3 – Have moderate amounts

You'll also be able to eat in smaller quantities: fresh fish (not shellfish), particularly salmon, mackerel, herring, trout or tuna, unsmoked (organic) tofu, olive oil, root vegetables, avocado, bananas, cherries, kiwi or other fruit,** vegetable and fruit juices of all veg and fruits allowed, puréed brown lentils, organic pure vinegars.

All food and drink should be organic, as fresh as you can have it and lightly cooked or raw.

Instructions

Follow the lists of foods and drinks above in organizing your own week's detox – having NO items from the first list, PLENTY from the second list and moderate amounts of items from the third list.

Have 3 meals a day – breakfast, lunch and an early evening meal – eating enough to satisfy the appetite but no more, and making sure menus are varied. Drink about 2½ litres (4 pints) of water or diluted fruit juice or herbal or green tea a day. During the detox, practise all you've learned in Step 1 and try to remain relaxed and calm.

* You may prefer to eliminate wheat products, such as wheat bread, pasta and couscous, as wheat is a fairly common cause of bloating.
** Citrus fruits and strawberries are quite acidic and may cause stomach gripes in some people on a detox diet. Avoid if this happens.

Three-day detox diet

The three-day menus below are typical of how you should be eating – don't forget plenty of additional water.

DAY 1

On rising:
water

Breakfast:
banana, melon and apple fruit salad
green tea

Lunch
large salad of lettuce, peppers, cucumber, tomato, celery and watercress, with fresh almonds and sunflower seeds, olive oil and cider vinegar dressing
pineapple juice

Evening
small piece of fresh salmon, poached, with broccoli, green beans, large portion of brown rice and sauce of puréed avocado with chopped cucumber and garlic stirred in
camomile tea.

DAY 2

On rising:
water

Breakfast
bowl of cherries, slice of melon, sunflower seeds
green tea

Lunch
lentil and carrot soup made by cooking brown lentils with carrots and onion in fresh vegetable stock or water and puréeing; serve with chopped coriander
organic rice cake
apple, water

Evening
portion brown rice mixed with chopped tomato, onion, basil and pine nuts (plus any other allowed items), mixed with olive oil and vinegar as before.
glass of cranberry juice
banana

DAY 3

On rising:
water

Breakfast
apple, slice of rye bread, handful of walnuts
green tea

Lunch
salad of raw baby spinach, rocket, watercress and sliced red pepper, tossed with silken tofu strips in olive oil and vinegar
piece of dark rye bread OR portion of brown rice
cranberry juice

Evening
small portion new potatoes, sliced and mixed with a salad of sliced tomatoes, onion, garlic, cucumber, mint, parsley, tossed in olive oil, lemon juice and sesame seed dressing
slice of cantaloupe melon

To speed up your detox

HERBAL SUPPLEMENTS Some herbs and supplements help. Aloe vera and milk thistle are most likely to (buy in tincture or capsule form), while dandelion, nettle, parsley, rosemary and thyme all help. Use fresh if you can, chop and make an infusion, like tea. Drink once or twice a day.

LYMPHATIC DRAINAGE MASSAGE The lymph system drains toxins (which is why the lymph nodes in the neck swell when immune system is stressed). Drainage can be helped with massage. A qualified holistic masseur will know how to massage to best effect. See the Appendix.

EXERCISE This helps the release of toxins in several ways – one, by increasing depth and rate of respiration so toxins are expelled in breath; two, by releasing toxins in sweat; and three, by stimulating lymph system and increasing urination. Try to take two walks daily while you detox.

Step 1 round-up

THE POINT OF STEP 1 HAS BEEN TO GET BACK TO YOUR 'REAL' CORE. TO RE-DISCOVER YOUR FOUNDATIONS, STRIPPED OF ALL THE RUBBISH THAT YOU'VE BEEN COLLECTING ALONG THE WAY THESE PAST YEARS.

• At the end of this Step you should feel calmer, grounded, relaxed. Lighter, brighter, more clear-headed and more familiar with your body. You should begin to feel that you can control your life, rather than have it controlling you. You should begin to feel that true energy is not just a dream, not just something for other people.

• You should be feeling released from negative ties, eager for change, eager for balance and eager to tackle Step 2, which will be completely concerned with energizing and strengthening your body, building brick upon brick on that level ground, on the firm foundations.

• At the end of Step 1, then, I would like you to think about your body and how you can come into Step 2 in the most positive way. What I would like you to do is: TALK, ASK, THINK.

• I would like you to talk (to others, to yourself) about how people see you and your body. What do they envy? What do they not envy? Think about what people say. Compare what they say with what you think about yourself. Think about your body. What do you want from it? (Health? Strength? Suppleness? Stamina? Something else?) What can you give it? (More time? More thought? More kindness? More hard work?)

• Think of some body goals for being, and some body goals for doing. Write your goals down. For example:

Being goals – I want my body to be dynamic, energetic, healthy, useful.

Doing goals – I want my body to climb a mountain, leap over a five-barred gate, scuba-dive with ease, run a marathon, or perhaps simply run for a bus without complaining.

Now say:

I can do this. I want to do this. I will do this.

....and move on to Step 2

step 2

Finding Physical Energy

Tuning the body to run smoothly and efficiently

In Step 2 we look at the mechanics of physical energy. The body is a chemical factory; energy is produced within this factory and scientists are finding out more and more about how the factory works.

In its simplest form, physical energy is the calories that we eat and drink, which the body converts into the ability to move and carry out its life-supporting functions like breathing and building tissue. However, consuming more calories won't necessarily give us extra energy – it may just make us fat and, indeed, decrease our energy levels.

For that extra energy we need to think of the body as an engine – and provide it with all it needs to be powerful and to run smoothly and to run efficiently. So we need to discover the key elements – the right petrol, the right oil, the right degree of maintenance – to produce those effects.

In Step 2 we look at how body strength, smoothness and efficiency come from several sources – good nutrition, good exercise and good health. These are not, generally, 'luck factors', but involve you making a conscious effort to look after your body every day.

In early life and young adulthood, our bodies often take a great deal of abuse and neglect without complaint. However, at a certain stage – often around 30 – this ceases to be the case and energy levels drop if we don't take responsibility for physical well-being. From that point on, you get out of your body in terms of energy what you put in in terms of care.

So in the pages ahead we discuss diet and nutrition, energy foods and supplements, and look at how and when – as well as what – to eat. We look at physical fitness and what effect that has on your energy. Lastly, we think about age and energy and whether getting older necessarily means a reduction in energy levels?

Your own degree of total attainable physical energy is, in part, defined by your genes – not all of us are born capable of being a triathlon champion or an Olympic gymnast, no matter how much care we give our bodies. Few of us will ever be able to muster enough stamina to exist on four hours' sleep a night as some people do. Your body has its own limitations, but within those limits you should go for total energy. Don't compare – just find out what YOU can do.

The great thing about physical energy is that once you get on the path to improving it, the results are quick – and often dramatic.

Power your body... build the strong walls and roof... Yes, you can do this too.

Week 2

General notes

Don't forget to continue with your regular:
- stretching
- yoga
- massage

this week.

Day 1

- Read through Step 2.
- Check your weight (see page 61).
- Using the Eating for Energy section (pages 60–71), makes notes on how your usual diet could be improved. For example, check the vitamin and minerals chart against the ingredients you actually normally eat.

Day 2

- Your Detox Diet finishes today, so plan yourself a complete week's menus of eating for energy (or use the 7-day menu set out on pages 77–80).
- Could you cut down on alcohol?
- Could you drink more water?
- Shop for what you need.

Day 3

- Carefully read the section entitled What to Eat When (see pages 68–72).
  Could you alter your eating patterns to give yourself a more even flow of energy?
- Do you have any of the symptoms of low blood sugar and could you increase the amount of low Glycaemic Index foods that you eat (see page 70)?
- Begin your new Eating Programme (pages 75–80).

Day 4

- Prepare to start your aerobic exercise programme as set out on pages 82–7).
- Check out local walks and work out their distance following the guidelines. Work out your maximum heart-rate and suitable training zone (see pages 84–5).
- Decide which method of checking your heart-rate you will use while training (see pages 84–5).
- Make sure you have equipped yourself with the right clothes, shoes and supplies (see page 85).

Day 5

- Do your first aerobic walking session. Walk 1 mile, keeping your heart-rate within your training zone. Record how long it takes you to cover the distance.
- Continue with the walking programme, at least 3 or 4 times a week.
- Plan these walks into your schedule.
- Don't forget to warm up and cool down properly before and after each exercise session.

Day 6

- Start your Strength Programme (page 88–95). Do 3 sessions a week from now on, preferably on alternate days from those on which you do your walks.
- Plan these sessions into your schedule.
- Don't forget to stretch out the muscles you have worked (see page 94–5).

Day 7

- Are you over 50? Read the Age and Energy section on pages 96–8).
- Read the Step 2 Round-up (page 99).

TURN THE PAGE TO START STEP TWO

2 Discover the nutritional keys that will help you to unlock your body's full energy potential. Not only what you eat, but also how you eat – and what you ought to avoid – are important factors in the energy equation.

eating for energy

good fuel is vital for efficient energy production in your body

Nutrients for energy

If your body is a factory, then the fuel it requires for energy is calories in the form of the food and drink it consumes. Over the next few pages we take a look at food intake and how it can affect your energy levels.

Human energy is measured in kilocalories – nowadays usually simply called calories. When you eat, you take in calories for fuel, and when you move, exercise – or simply exist – you burn up calories for fuel. All food and most drinks supply these calories – only water is calorie-free.

How many calories do I need?

The amount of calories you consume will affect your energy levels. Get too few for your body's needs and the calorie deficit will produce weight loss, physical weakness and muscle wastage, and various attendant health problems. Serious calorie deficiency will eventually cause death from malnutrition and accompanying complications.

Consume too many calories for your body's needs, however, and the surplus will be stored as body fat, resulting in weight gain and, eventually, obesity and the many health problems it may bring, such as heart disease, arthritis, diabetes and, eventually, what is called 'morbid obesity', with inability to move or function normally, and early death. So you can see quite clearly that getting your calorie consumption about right is crucial to good health and energy levels.

Desirable height / weight limits for men and women

This chart is based on the internationally accepted body mass index system and shows lower and upper limits for healthy weight. If you are within the range for your height then you needn't worry about your calorie intake; if you weigh less – or much more – than the levels given, however, then your calorie intake and weight may be beginning to affect your energy levels. If you are too low a weight you should increase your calories; too heavy, you should decrease them until you are within range. Tips for achieving this easily appear on page 76.

Height (no shoes)		Weight (no clothes) Lower limit		Upper limit	
5ft	(1.52m)	7st 4lb	(46.3kg)	8st 12lb	(56.25kg)
5ft 1in	(1.55m)	7st 7lb	(47.75kg)	9st 3lb	(58.5kg)
5ft 2in	(1.58m)	7st 10lb	(49kg)	9st 6lb	(60kg)
5ft 3in	(1.6m)	8st	(50.75kg)	9st 11lb	(62.25kg)
5ft 4in	(1.63m)	8st 4lb	(52.75kg)	10st 2lb	(64.5kg)
5ft 5in	(1.65m)	8st 8lb	(54.5kg)	10st 6lb	(66.25kg)
5ft 6in	(1.68m)	8st 11lb	(56kg)	10st 11lb	(68.5kg)
5ft 7in	(1.7m)	9st 1lb	(57.75kg)	11st 2lb	(70.75kg)
5ft 8in	(1.73m)	9st 5lb	(59.5kg)	11st 7lb	(73kg)
5ft 9in	(1.75m)	9st 8lb	(61kg)	11st 12lb	(75.25kg)
5ft 10in	(1.78m)	9st 13lb	(63kg)	12st 3lb	(77.75kg)
5ft 11in	(1.8m)	10st 3lb	(65kg)	12st 8lb	(80kg)
6ft	(1.83m)	10st 7lb	(66.75kg)	12st 13lb	(82.25kg)
6ft 1in	(1.85m)	10st 11lb	(68.5kg)	13st 4lb	(84.5kg)
6ft 2in	(1.88m)	11st 1lb	(70.5kg)	13st 9lb	(86.75kg)
6ft 3in	(1.91m)	11st 5lb	(72.25kg)	14st	(89kg)

Between the two extremes, however, there's plenty of room for manoeuvre. It's estimated that an average adult man needs 2,550 calories a day to maintain reasonable weight and cover all normal calorie usage, and an average woman needs only about 1,940.

However, this varies considerably according to work done (activity – see later), height, age and other factors. Also, a normal weight range for two people of the same sex and height can be as much two stones. For example, a 35-year-old woman 5ft 6in in height can weigh as little as 8st 11lb or as much as 10st 11lb and yet still be considered an acceptable healthy weight.

Nutrients explained

Although all food supplies calories, not all calories come in the same form. In order to survive and thrive, we need various different nutrients, each of which performs different functions in the body. These are macronutrients – the bulky items that form the majority of what we eat – and the micronutrients – the smaller elements that we can hardly see, and mostly can hardly taste. Most foods are a mixture of macro- and micronutrients in varying proportions.

A deficiency of any one of the nutrients can be detrimental to good body functioning, but some are more important than others. Here we look at the various nutrients, their role in the body, their effect on energy levels and which foods are good sources of each.

Carbohydrates 50–60 per cent of the calories in your diet should come from carbohydrates, which are the fuel of preference for supplying the body with 'instant' energy. When we eat carbohydrate, it is broken down in the digestive system and absorbed very, or quite, quickly (depending upon the complexity of the structure of the food and other factors) into the bloodstream as energy.

This food group is subdivided into starches and sugars and the majority of the carbohydrate that we eat should be starch. Starches are found in plant-based foods, such as cereals, bread, pulses and root vegetables, and for health it is important to eat these 'complex carbohydrates', as they are called, in a natural or near-natural state, rather than highly refined. Other vegetables contain starch in varying quantities, but there is hardly any in most fruits, which tend to contain the other type of carbohydrate – sugars. Vegetables also contain some sugars. The sugars found naturally in fruits and vegetables form part of your healthy carbohydrate intake.

Most of us eat too much 'refined starch' in the form of processed cakes, biscuits, desserts, and so on, and in refined sugar. Mostly because of their fairly simple structure, these refined carbohydrates provide energy which is quickly usable by the body. This can be handy in certain limited circumstances, for example in sport. An extremely refined form of carbohydrate is glucose, which can be absorbed and used as energy within minutes of eating or drinking it, compared with the two hours or so it takes for the body to begin to use the starch contained in a plate of brown lentils.

So you see that for a constant stream of long-term energy you are better off with the complex carbohydrates forming the majority of your meals, with just a small intake of sugars and other refined carbohydrates to provide short-term energy. This is discussed further in the box on What to Eat When on page 69. See also the section on Fibre on page 67.

If you eat more carbohydrate than you need for energy, the surplus will be converted into fat and stored in the body's fat cells.

Protein is the 'smart nutrient' that the body uses to build muscle, to repair tissue, maintain cells, regulate many body functions, and more. Therefore adequate protein is essential for good health, strength, fitness and energy. About 10–15 per cent of your calorie intake should be in the form of protein, depending upon various factors including the amount of exercise you take and how much muscle your body contains.

Protein is made up of amino acids, 22 of which are used in the body. Different food sources contain different mixes of these amino acids and so a diet which contains a variety of different types of protein-rich foods will ensure that the body receives all the amino acids it needs.

Protein-rich food sources are meats, pulses, dairy produce, eggs, fish, poultry and nuts, but many foods contain reasonable amounts of protein – including many 'starch' foods, such as potatoes, bread, pasta and various wholegrains.

If your protein intake exceeds your body's needs for making muscle and the other functions described above, it can be converted into glucose and used for energy. If your body has no use for this surplus energy it will then be converted and stored as body fat. Protein takes longer than carbohydrate to be absorbed by the body and converted into energy, and is thus a useful food for long-term energy and keeping blood sugar levels even.

Fat comes in three main types – saturated, polyunsaturated and monounsaturated – is found in a wide range of foods and is our main source of long-term energy, being digested more slowly than carbohydrate or protein and then converted into glucose or, if not needed for energy, stored as body fat. It is also important as a carrier of vitamins A and D – the fat-soluble vitamins.

About 30 per cent of your calorie intake should be in the form of fat, proportions of which can be divided roughly evenly between the three types. Most foods contain all three types of fat, in varying amounts.

• SATURATED FAT is the kind that is linked with increased risk of heart disease, stroke and other ills, and is found mainly in dairy produce, meat and eggs, as well as in processed foods like pies, pastries, biscuits, cakes and so on. Processed foods may also be high in trans fats – fats which have been altered by processing to be solid at room temperatures and which are similar to saturated fat – indeed, they may be linked even more closely with health problems than saturated fat.

• POLYUNSATURATED FAT is found in greatest quantities in a variety of plant oils, including corn, safflower, sunflower and nut and seed oils. This group of fats contains what are called the essential fatty acids (EFAs), linoleic acid and alpha linolenic acid, types of polyunsaturated fat that are vital for good health, a healthy immune system and energy conversion. There is mounting evidence to show that many of us fall short of enough of the EFAs in our diets, and a shortfall of EFAs may be closely linked with certain cases of low energy levels. Related to alpha linolenic acid are the fatty acids EPA and DHA, found in highest quantities in oily fish and fish oils. These are all important in helping to maintain a healthy circulatory system.

• MONOUNSATURATED FAT is found in greatest quantities in olives, olive oil, rapeseed oil, groundnut oil and other plant oils, nuts, seeds and avocados. Some experts believe that the majority of our fat

NOTE: Vitamins and minerals not mentioned in the chart – e.g. vitamin K, phosphorous, sodium – are present in the average diet in more than adequate quantities for health, although see notes on salt intake and sports on page 72.

The major vitamins

Vitamins	Good sources	What it does
Vitamin A	Offal, cod liver oil, dairy produce, orange-fleshed and dark green fruits and vegetables*	Essential for healthy vision, eyes, skin and growth;. toxic in excess.
B Group	Yeast extract, wholegrains, fortified cereals, meat, nuts, fish	Six water-soluble vitamins essential for growth, healthy nervous system, body maintenance, food digestion and metabolism
Vitamin C	Citrus fruits, berry fruits, peppers, green leafy vegetables and most fruit and vegetables	Antioxidant, also vital for building healthy tissue, bones and wound healing; helps iron absorption, immune system
Vitamin D	Cod liver oil, oily fish, margarine, fortified cereals, sunlight	Vital to help absorption of calcium and phosphorous for bones, etc.
Vitamin E	Plant oils, nuts, seeds, avocados	Antioxidant; blood-thinner, anti-ageing, aids healing process, skin renewal

* As carotenoids converted into vitamin A in the body.

intake should come from this group – and, certainly, it seems to have no contraindications. Oils high in monounsaturates also tend to be high in the antioxidant vitamin E (see table opposite).

To achieve a good balance of the different types of fat, most people need to eat more plant foods and fewer animal and dairy foods. Fats are also energy-rich – containing 9 calories per gram compared with fewer than 4 calories per gram for carbohydrate and 4 for protein. If you have a tendency to overweight, therefore, it is wise to cut down on animal and dairy fats first.

Alcohol is not necessary for a healthy body, but it is grouped with the macronutrients as it is the only other source of calories in the diet, containing 7 calories per gram. Small amounts of alcohol, particularly red wine and dark beers, are linked with protection against heart disease. However, as alcohol is a depressant and

The major minerals

Minerals	Good sources	What it does
Calcium	Dairy produce, leafy greens, nuts, seeds, fortified cereals and bread	Bone formation, healthy nervous system, muscle function
Iodine	Dairy produce, seafood, seaweed	Thyroid functioning
Iron	Dark leafy greens, red meat, pulses, offal, eggs, nuts, wholegrains	Oxygenates blood, health of red blood cells, resistance to infection, healing
Magnesium	Nuts, seeds, wholegrains, green vegetables	Bone maintenance, helps release energy, regulation of muscles and nerves
Potassium	Fresh fruits and vegetables, pulses, nuts, dried fruits	Regulates body fluids, nerves, heartbeat, blood pressure, diuretic
Selenium	Brazil nuts, brown lentils, fish, seeds, pork	Antioxidant, healthy thyroid, normal growth, fertility
Zinc	Wheatgerm, nuts, seeds, red meat, seaweed, seafood	Antioxidant, growth and repair, skin health, fertility, immune system

addictive, contains very few useful nutrients except calories, can lead to weight gain and dependency, intake in excess of a glass or two a day is not recommended. Excess alcohol intake is damaging to many body functions, and can reduce energy levels significantly, partly by disrupting sleep and also because it causes fluctuating blood sugar levels rather in the same way that a high intake of refined sugar will. Further information on alcohol and energy appears in other parts of this book.

Micronutrients Vitamins, minerals and other trace elements found in food are important in many ways. Many aid in energy conversion and help build or maintain healthy tissue, bone and blood.

Some are antioxidants, helping to keep us healthy and fit by 'mopping up' metabolism (energy production) by-products called free radicals, which can contribute to ill-health, including heart disease and cancer, ageing and all kinds of cell damage. Free radicals may be produced in excess because of pollution (e.g. from cigarette smoke or alcohol or atmospheric pollution), through stress, through high levels of exercise, and so on. Vitamins C and E are antioxidants, as is the mineral selenium.

Also many of the so-called 'phytochemicals' now being discovered in hundreds of different vegetables and fruits are antioxidants. One of the first of these to be discovered was beta-carotene, the orange pigment in carrots and tomatoes. We now know that eating a wide and plentiful supply of different fruits and vegetables – especially dark green, red and orange ones – may be our wisest health insurance of all.

See the charts on the previous pages.

Fibre Scientifically termed non-starch polysaccharides, fibre is the component in plant foods which isn't absorbed into the small intestines during the digestive process but is fermented in the bowel.

There are two types of fibre. *Insoluble fibre* is found mainly in whole wheat, corn, brown rice, vegetables and pulses and helps to 'bulk up' the stools and speed elimination – thus adequate insoluble fibre in the diet may help you to feel more energetic by preventing the sluggish, bloated full feeling that can come with constipation. *Soluble fibre* is found mainly in pulses, oats, rye, apples, citrus and other fruits and can help to reduce levels of cholesterol in the bloodstream.

Both types of fibre can also help to regulate blood sugar and thus help to maintain a constant energy flow and help prevent hunger, as fibre-rich foods tend to have a low Glycaemic Index (see the box overleaf on What to Eat When). A varied diet rich in pulses, wholegrains, fruits and vegetables will ensure that you get enough of both types of fibre.

Water and other drinks Water contains hardly any nutrients – apart from traces of minerals, which vary considerably according to source. It is, however, vital for life and energy. If you don't drink enough, the body becomes dehydrated and with that comes weakness, lassitude, dizziness and fainting, depending upon the degree of dehydration.

Most of us need about 4 pints (2.25 litres) of water – or other hydrating drinks, such as watered-down fruit juice or herbal drinks – a day. Many other everyday drinks are actually dehydrating and can't be counted towards the day's fluid intake – caffeine-rich drinks, such as coffee, cocoa and cola, black tea, and alcohol are all dehydrating.

In certain circumstances we need more than 4 pints – for example, in hot conditions, if we exercise a lot or have taken a lot of salt-rich food.

It is estimated that most people drink only about a quarter of the fluid they really should take in every day for the maintenance of good health, proper metabolic functioning and the prevention of dehydration.

Some drinks, of course, provide us with nutrients as well as with hydration – whole milk, for example, contains both protein and calcium, as well as various vitamins, fat and calories. Fruit juices contain fruit sugars (fructose), as well as vitamins, minerals and calories. And so on.

For more on drinks for sport, see page 72.

If all that sounds very complicated, take heart! The basic message of nutrition for energy can be quickly summed up in just a few simple pointers:

- Eat a varied diet containing adequate calories – if you are gaining or losing weight you will know whether your calorie intake/output balance is wrong.
- Eat few highly processed and refined foods and eat more whole foods.
- Eat a diet high in fresh fruit and vegetables – five portions a day are advised.
- Eat a diet high in other plant foods – wholegrain cereals, pulses, nuts and seeds.
- Instead of a diet rich in high-saturated-fat foods like meats, dairy produce and hard fats, eat more fish (especially oily fish), pulses and plant oils.
- Cut down on your alcohol (and tea and coffee) consumption and drink much more water.

The information set out on the following pages will help you to build up a high-energy diet in more practical ways.

What to eat when

Eating for energy is not just about what types of food to eat, but also how, and when, to eat. The guide here explains how to maximize your nutrients and calories.

Meal distribution

The best way to eat is to spread your calorie consumption fairly evenly throughout the day for a constant supply of energy. The ideal way is to have three small to medium-sized meals and two or three small snacks, going no more than 2½ hours without food.

Most people don't eat enough at breakfast time – when after, perhaps, 12 hours without food, your blood sugar levels (see the Glycaemic Index, page 70) are low and your body and brain NEED sustenance! If you skip breakfast you may feel light-headed and unable to concentrate during the morning. Lunch and evening meal should be about the same size, though with a different balance of nutrients (see below). It is sometimes said that your evening meal should be the smallest of the day, but I believe this is wrong – avoid huge meals late at night, which may cause indigestion during the night, but a reasonable meal taken between 7 and 8 in the evening is a good idea as it is a long time until breakfast! A snack before bedtime, of milk and a plain biscuit, is good if you tend towards insomnia.

Be guided by your own common sense when it comes to what you eat – if feeling genuinely hungry, have a snack of some low G.I. food. Don't have a highly refined sugar snack as this will leave you feeling even hungrier before long.

Meal balance

It pays to give attention to the balance of nutrients in each meal. Carbs, proteins and fats all have their part to play at certain times of day and may govern, at least in part, how energetic you feel.

Breakfast should contain carbohydrate, fat and protein in more or less equal amounts, and the carbohydrate content should include both starch and sugar. Such a breakfast means that you get 'instant energy' from the sugar, slightly less instant energy from the starch, and longer-lasting energy from the fat and protein. A typical breakfast to achieve this would be orange juice (sugar), high fruit and nut muesli (starch, fat and a little protein and sugar), skimmed milk (protein and sugar), and a small slice of wholewheat bread (starch and a little fat). Such a breakfast would last you throughout a hard morning.

Lunch should be the meal of the day that contains most protein and least starch, as experiments consistently show that a high-carbohydrate meal taken at lunchtime creates drowsiness or sluggishness in the afternoon and inhibits both physical and mental performance. This is due to the fact that carbohydrates stimulate the production of the calming chemical serotonin, as discussed in Step 1, and starch – particularly refined starch, such as white bread – seems to have the greatest effect. So an ideal lunch would be a cheese salad with just a small slice of wholemeal bread or rye crispbreads, followed by fruit, for example. The wrong kind of lunch would be a plate of spaghetti followed by a sticky pudding.

Evening is the time to enjoy your carbs – they will help you relax and sleep better, and help to ensure that you get enough carbohydrate during your day. It is best to choose your carbs from the lower end of the Glycaemic Index to help avoid hunger pangs during the night. A brown rice and vegetable curry with pulses would be ideal.

Between-meal snacks should be rich in vitamins, minerals, essential fatty acids and antioxidants. This is an ideal time to catch up on your fruit intake – a piece of fresh fruit high in vitamin C, some nuts high in vitamin E and EFAs, some dried fruit high in iron, for example. With these types of foods you will also be getting more fibre. Forget the crisps and chocolate bars – choose power snacks for health and energy.

Eating nutrients that work together

Some different nutrients like to be eaten with each other, while others prefer to be eaten apart – and if you know a few simple rules you will enhance the beneficial effect of what you eat without trouble.

- Iron absorption is helped if you take vitamin C at the same time – so have an orange with your baked beans, or some spring greens with your lean beef, or grapefruit before your boiled egg.
- A diet high in essential fatty acids may help the absorption of calcium, so foods or meals which contain both are ideal – e.g. muesli and milk, nuts and cheese, or almonds (these contain both).
- Various foods hinder absorption of calcium, iron and zinc – including tea and coffee (due to tannin content), bran (due to phytates), and rhubarb, spinach, chard, chocolate and beetroot, due to the oxylates they contain. Avoid drinking tea and coffee with meals, avoid sprinkling bran on meals, and go easy on high-oxylate foods.

What to eat when

RULE 1 – Eat 'little to medium' and often.
RULE 2 – Eat a bigger breakfast.
RULE 3 – If you feel hungry, eat something nutritious.
RULE 4 – Avoid a high-carb lunch.
RULE 5 – Your evening meal should be high in complex carbohydrates.
RULE 6 – Snack on nutritious foods between meals.

Blood sugar levels, energy and the Glycaemic Index

Fluctuating levels of glucose (sugar) in the blood are a common cause of low energy levels. If your blood sugar is low (hypoglycaemia) you may feel tired, dizzy and unable to concentrate, perhaps with a craving for sweet food. Low blood sugar can be caused by skipping meals, prolonged exercise without sustenance, or a high-sugar (or high-alcohol) diet which causes the body to release extra insulin – which may then cause blood sugar levels to dip too low. Some women tend to experience low blood sugar more before their period, and caffeine may exacerbate the problem. There is evidence that a chromium deficiency may cause low blood sugar. If this is the case, ensure adequate chromium in the diet by eating plenty of chromium-rich foods, such as shellfish, cheese, whole grains and pulses.

The Glycaemic Index measures the rate at which blood glucose levels rise after different carbohydrate foods are eaten. Glucose itself has a GI rating of 100 – the quickest carb to be absorbed – so the nearer to 100 a food's rating is, the higher its Glycaemic Index. Plenty of low-GI foods in every meal will help sustain even blood glucose levels and sustain energy throughout the day. It will also help keep hunger pangs at bay. Fat and protein aren't measured on the GI, but both behave in the body like low-GI foods, so if you eat a little of both at each meal it will help keep blood glucose levels even.

If you feel you have low blood sugar, the worst thing you can do is eat a high-sugar snack on its own. NOTE: Hypoglycaemia in diabetics is beyond the scope of this book and needs to be discussed with a physician.

LOW-GI FOODS FOR LONG-TERM ENERGY

- All pulses, including lentils, chickpeas, soya beans, baked beans, kidney beans, butter beans, borlotti beans, etc. Barley
- Apples, dried apricots, peaches, plums, cherries, grapefruit
- Avocados, courgettes, spinach, peppers, onions, mushrooms, leafy greens, leeks, broad beans, green beans, sprouts, mange-tout peas, cauliflower, broccoli
- Natural yoghurt, sweetened yoghurt, milk, peanuts

MEDIUM-GI FOODS FOR MID-TERM ENERGY

- Sweet potatoes, boiled potatoes, yams, raw carrots, sweetcorn, peas
- All types of pasta, (white and wholewheat), oats, porridge, oatmeal biscuits, All Bran, noodles
- Whole-grain rye bread, pitta, buckwheat, bulgar wheat, white and brown rice
- Grapes, oranges, kiwi, mangoes, beetroot, fresh dates, figs, apple-and-date bars

HIGH-GI FOODS FOR SHORT-TERM IMMEDIATE ENERGY

- Glucose, sugar, honey, pineapple, bananas, raisins, watermelon
- Baked potatoes, mashed potatoes, parsnips, cooked carrots, squash, swede
- Rye and wheat crispbreads, cream crackers, wholemeal bread, white bread, rice cakes, couscous
- Cornflakes, Bran Flakes, instant oat cereal, popcorn, muffins, crumpets
- Orange squash, dried dates

Increased needs

Some nutrients – and alcohol – increase the need in your diet for other nutrients.

- A high-sodium diet, when you have a taste for salty foods, increases the need for potassium in your diet. It's best to cut down on salty foods for your health – and to avoid fluid retention – but, otherwise, increase your intake of fresh fruits and vegetables as these are high in potassium.
- A high intake of phosphorous (likely if you eat a lot of processed foods) increases your need for calcium.
- A high alcohol intake increases the need for a variety of nutrients, including vitamin C, B group, A and D, zinc, calcium, phosphorous, magnesium and essential fatty acids.

Increasing the nutrient content of your shopping

It pays to look after your food, in order to retain maximum vitamins. Buy food as fresh as possible, especially fruit and vegetables. Don't buy food that has been kept in warm conditions and/or in sunlight, or if it is bruised or shrivelled. Light, heat and damage destroy vitamins C and B.

Take food home as soon as possible and store it in cool dark conditions, preferably in the fridge. Eat well before the 'use by' date. Don't prepare salads or cut fruit long before you are to eat them as vitamin C is destroyed this way, too. Eat plenty of your fruit and veg raw or very lightly cooked, as cooking destroys vitamins. Steaming and microwaving are the two best methods for retaining water-soluble vitamins in your food.

Eating for exercise and sport

Professional sportspeople have their own strategies for nutrition – carb loading, protein sparing and various other techniques – which are really beyond the scope of this book. If you get fit enough and energetic enough to want to exercise or to play any sport at a professional level, then you will need specialist advice (see the Appendix), but for the majority of us, who are simply building more regular exercise into our lives, a few general guidelines will suffice:

- An hour or so before a major exercise session (e.g. an hour or so in the gym), have a small meal containing some carb food high on the Glycaemic Index and some carb food that rates medium or low on the Index. This will provide quick energy for when you start to exercise and will sustain you throughout an hour or so of moderate to hard exercise. A banana (high) and an apple (medium-low) would be ideal.
- If about to start a longer session of moderate exercise (e.g. a walk lasting several hours), you need a meal containing short- and long-term sustenance, therefore follow the guidelines for Breakfast above.

• For any exercise session lasting longer than a few minutes you will need a supply of hydrating drink – water or water with a dash of fruit juice will be fine for any sessions lasting less than 90 minutes. If buying commercial drinks, look for the words 'isotonic' or 'hypotonic' for use before and during a sports session as they will quickly rehydrate you. Very long sessions in heat (e.g. a long walk on a hot day) will mean that you should add some salt to the drink to replace that lost in perspiration and to aid absorption of fluid.

If you don't rehydrate yourself regularly during exercise you are likely to feel weak, dizzy and perhaps faint.

After exercise, ensure you drink plenty and have a high-carb snack to replace lost energy quickly if you feel tired. If buying a commercial drink, choose one labelled 'hypertonic', which will be higher in glucose to aid recovery than the iso- or hypotonic drinks. During prolonged exercise you may also need to have a high-carb snack, such as a banana.

While on the subject of exercise and food, I should point out that you shouldn't overcompensate for your exercise session by pigging out, especially if you are overweight or watching your weight. For example, an average one-hour session at the gym burns up only about 250 calories – equivalent to a small chocolate bar or a very small sandwich.

Do you need supplements?

A small fortune is spent daily throughout the world by people buying vitamins and other food supplements. Can they really help you to better health? Which ones might increase your energy – or are they all a waste of money?

Vitamin and mineral supplements

If you're feeling a bit below par, you may be forgiven for feeling that a couple of fizzy vitamin C pills or a course of iron tablets may put you right. Most of us buy vitamin pills now and then; others use a wide range all the time. The rationale seems to be that if a certain amount of a vitamin is necessary, then twice as much is going to reap you twice the benefit.

Sadly, however, this is rarely the case, and 'overdosing' can often do more harm than good. If your diet is poor, you should take steps to improve it rather than try to correct the damage with a daily multivitamin. It is also true that if your normal diet is varied and healthy, following the guidelines earlier in this Step, then extra vitamins shouldn't be necessary. However, there are exceptions.

If you are ill or convalescing, under a lot of stress, you drink or smoke or are exercising hard, it may be a good idea to take a vitamin

C supplement, as all these situations tend to use up extra vitamin C and the official recommended daily amount at 40mg is quite low. It may also be wise to take a vitamin B complex supplement, as this water-soluble group of vitamins can also be lost for similar reasons.

If you are under par, a zinc supplement will help to build your immune system and prevent illness.

In fact, extra intake of most of the antioxidant vitamins and minerals – C, E and selenium – is probably a good idea if you are physically very active, as they help to prevent cell damage. Vitamin E, in addition, is necessary for the body's process of tissue repair. (However, supplements of the antioxidant beta-carotene are not thought to be a good idea.)

Omega-3 fish oil supplements may help to prevent joint damage.

Self-dosing with iron supplements isn't a good idea. If you think you are tired due to anaemia, see your doctor. In general, if you think you may need a supplement, or if you think you are ill or have any symptoms that you can't account for, you should see a doctor anyway. If you really need vitamin or mineral supplements, he or she will prescribe them in the correct dose.

Other supplements

If you care about your health, it is tempting to think that you can buy it in a jar of algae, or that you can get amazing energy with nothing more than a course of ginseng. Here we look at some of the food supplements most often taken to enhance energy.

Amino acids Protein is made up of amino acids, each of which has its own role to play within the body. If we eat sufficient protein for our needs, it is unlikely that taking any one particular amino acid will help, but L-carnitine is often taken as an aid to fat-burning, and arginine as an aid to building muscle. If you are a body-builder or working out in the gym for hours a day, it is possible that arginine might help you, but otherwise the amino acid supplements are probably best left on the shelf.

Co-enzyme Q10 This is sold as a supplement to help the body convert food into energy and for a variety of other apparent effects. Q10 occurs naturally in food and our bodies can also manufacture their own, but proponents say that when we are ill, or get old, this process maybe faulty. There is little scientific evidence for taking the supplement.

Gingko biloba This helps the flow of blood to the brain and is sold as an aid to memory, alertness and concentration. It may also help with circulatory problems in general. See also Mental Stamina, page 124.

Ginseng Used in the East as a tonic for thousands of years, panax ginseng (sometimes known as Korean ginseng) – the classic form of ginseng and reputed to be the 'best' – is said to stimulate physical performance and is frequently used by athletes. It is also said to help beat fatigue and mental stress. Ginseng shouldn't be taken by pregnant women or if you have high blood pressure, and should be taken only for a few weeks at a time. Evidence of ginseng's worth is mostly anecdotal – though there is plenty of it.

Kelp A type of seaweed that is rich in iodine and therefore said to help stimulate the thyroid gland. An underactive thyroid can be responsible for various symptoms, including mental tiredness, coldness, physical lethargy, weight gain, dry skin, puffy eyes and hair loss. If you think you may have an under-active thyroid it is best to see a doctor and get it checked. Avoid kelp if you have an over-active thyroid.

Royal jelly This is the sole food fed to the queen bee, who lives much longer than her worker bees. Claims for its effects on humans include increased lifespan, stamina, fertility and as a general tonic. Manufacturers say it needs to be taken for at least 2–3 months before any effect is noticed. Again, evidence for its efficacy is mostly anecdotal.

Wheat grass Can be bought at juice counters as a (nasty-tasting!) drink rich in vitamins, minerals and antioxidants. It is an expensive way of getting your nutrients.

Blue-green algae Available in capsule tablet form from health food shops, this again, weight for weight, is a good source of vitamins and minerals, but probably not taken in sufficient quantity by most people to make much real difference to their health.

St John's Wort This plant (*Hypericum performatum*) is known to be mildly anti-depressant and so, if depression is causing fatigue and lack of energy, then a course of the tincture taken three times daily may help. It is certainly worth trying. It may also help with menopausal and pre-menstrual symptoms.

Recommended daily supplement doses

VITAMIN C: 500–1,000mg; VITAMIN E: 400 iu; SELENIUM: 200 ug; `ZINC: 15mg; OMEGA-3 FISH OILS: 1,200 mg EPA/DHA.
(There is no collective recommended maximum for VITAMIN B group.)

2

Turn theory into practice with this easy seven-day menu that will get you started on the track to total physical energy. You will know this way of eating is right when you notice the start of positive changes in your body.

the eating programme

eating for energy is simple – and delicious –when you know how

The seven-day menu that follows is a blueprint for how you should be eating for energy. Try it, and then enjoy devising your own meals based on what you've learnt in the preceding pages. There are plenty of tips on making your meals interesting throughout.

The seven days of menus show ideas for the three main meals of the day. Read through the introductory pages, as they tell you all you need to know about extra snacks, drinks, portion sizes and so on.

Unlimited throughout the plan

- Fresh fruits and vegetables (though starchy vegetables, such as potatoes and sweet potatoes, should be limited unless you are trying to gain weight).
- Water.
- Fresh herbs and spices, garlic, vinegar.

Drinks

Drink at least 4 pints (2.25 litres) of water a day. This can be flavoured with fruit juice if you like. Other good drinks are herbal teas, green tea, a few cups of weakish ordinary tea a day. Coffee is best made in a filter machine, limited to 3 cups a day and avoided in the 6 hours before bedtime.

Allow yourself half a pint (300 ml) or so of skimmed or semi-skimmed milk a day as a drink on its own or in your tea and coffee. If you don't have this milk, eat natural yoghurt or take calcium supplements.

Avoid alcohol, except for the occasional glass of wine or beer.

Snacks

Have 2 between-meal snacks a day, preferably evenly spaced out between breakfast and lunch, and lunch and evening meal. These snacks should be a choice of the following, or similar (think nuts, seeds, fresh fruit, dried fruit, cereals).

- Fresh unsalted nuts and a piece of fresh fruit. (Especially good nuts are brazils, walnuts, almonds.)
- Handful of sunflower seeds and some dried ready-to-eat apricots.
- Natural bio yoghurt with fresh fruit chopped in.
- Small banana sandwich made with rye bread and a little spread.
- Oatcake and a few ready-to-eat prunes.
- Handful of pumpkin seeds and one or two dried figs or prunes.

Portion sizes

No portion sizes have been given, as you need to eat to suit your own hunger and activity levels. Use your common sense and eat enough to satisfy yourself but no more. You can always eat extra between-meal snacks if you are hungry (see above).

Try to eat a good breakfast and in the evening give yourself plenty of the carbohydrate element of the meal (potatoes, pasta, rice, etc.). Portions of fresh vegetables and salad items should be large rather than small. If watching your weight, see the next item.

Weight watching

If you are overweight, limit the amount of saturated fat and refined produce in your diet.

In the 7-day plan these are already quite low and you may find simply by following the plan and giving yourself medium portions you will lose weight. If further calorie reduction is needed, reduce the portion sizes slightly more, especially of red meat, cheese, oil and nuts – but don't cut them out altogether as you need the nutrients. You can, if you like, cut out breakfast bread when it is listed in addition to cereal.

If you are underweight, increase the amount of nuts and seeds and complex carbohydrates that you eat (pulses, cereals, root vegetables, etc.) and get extra plant oils in dressings. Increase portion sizes across the board. If poor appetite is a problem here, instead increase the amount of snacks that you eat (dried fruit and nuts are high in calories), and drink semi-skimmed milk between meals too, if you can.

Food tips

- Don't be afraid to experiment in the kitchen – today's cookbooks have plenty of exciting ways with pulses, fish, grains and so on.
- Don't stick with the same old favourites: instead of, say, rice, choose another grain instead – bulghar (cracked wheat) or quinoa

(a small high-protein grain from South America), for example. All grains are easy to cook and, anyway, instructions are on the packet.

• Ready-cooked canned pulses are easy and quick to use – drain them well before use.

• Keep a good storecupboard stocked with a range of spice pastes, whole spices (grind as you use them) and herbs to enliven casseroles, soups, stir-fries and so on. Well worth having are harissa paste (a fiery chilli-and-garlic mixture common in Moroccan cooking), garam masala, tahini (sesame-seed paste, flavourful and rich in essential fats, ideal with pulses) and saffron strands to add flavour and colour to all kinds of grain dishes and sauces to accompany fish and chicken and in soups. Completely indispensable are tomato sauce, tomato purée, canned tomatoes and passata.

• Try to keep some fresh herbs – almost all are high in healthful antioxidants and other natural plant chemicals. Also, you can't be without garlic or fresh chillies.

• In the fridge, keep fresh chilled bean and vegetable soups for emergencies; fresh stock and one or two bowls of fresh salads – all of which can be bought from the supermarket if you haven't time to make your own.

• Keep well stocked up on fresh fruit, vegetables and salads – remember, these are unlimited on the diet plan.

Seven-day eating plan

Day 1

Breakfast

Luxury muesli (high in fruit and nuts) with skimmed milk, topped with chopped cantaloupe melon or mango or orange

Slice of wholemeal bread with honey

Lunch

Grilled aubergine salad (aubergines sliced, brushed with olive oil, seasoned and grilled until charred), served with slices of goats' cheese and mixed salad leaves

1 banana

OR

Two free-range eggs scrambled and served on rye bread

Brazil nuts

I orange

Evening

I small snapper (or other small whole fish), grilled or barbecued and served with a tahini sauce (light tahini beaten with lemon juice, olive oil and crushed garlic to taste), baked fennel, olive oil mashed potato OR

Wholewheat pizza base topped with tomato sauce, sliced mozzarella, thinly sliced vegetables (e.g. mushroom, red onion) and olive oil, and baked; mixed salad

Day 2

Breakfast

1/2 grapefruit OR portion berry fruits

Bowlful of traditional porridge sprinkled with honey and served with skimmed milk

Slice of wholemeal bread with a little spread and Marmite

Lunch

Salad of shelled walnuts, sliced avocado and crumbled Feta cheese, tossed with baby spinach, rocket, watercress and extra-virgin olive oil, balsamic vinegar and seasoning

OR

Fresh carrot and coriander soup with Feta stirred in

1 small slice of rye bread

Individual tub of fromage frais with honey

Evening meal

Easy chicken and chickpea tagine (brown some skinned chicken thighs and chopped onion in groundnut oil and casserole for l hour with ground cumin, canned tomatoes, chicken stock, canned chickpeas, and a few dried apricots and harissa paste to taste), garnished with flaked almonds; bulghar wheat or couscous to serve (you could use lean lamb fillet instead of chicken) OR

Lentil and butternut squash tagine (cubed squash browned with chopped onion in groundnut oil and casseroled with puy lentils for1 hour with ground cumin, coriander and cinnamon to taste, canned tomatoes, vegetable stock, chopped fresh chillies, pine nuts), garnished with fresh coriander and served with bulghar wheat or couscous.

l banana

Day 3

Breakfast

Boiled egg(s) with wholemeal bread and spread; orange juice OR

Tub of 8%-fat fromage frais, honey, oat bran flakes, chopped peach or orange

Lunch

Salad of fresh, lightly grilled or canned tuna with cannellini beans, black olives, wedges of little gem lettuce, tomato, sliced red onion and garlic drizzled with olive oil and balsamic vinegar, seasoned to taste

OR

Baked potato filled with lentil dhal, drizzled with natural bio yoghurt and garnished with chopped mild chilli and salad

Evening meal

Pasta of choice cooked and tossed with cooked broad beans, crumbled grilled lean bacon, watercress, chopped mint, flat-leaved parsley, olive oil, lemon juice and seasoning to taste

OR

Pasta of choice, cooked and served with a rich tomato sauce, chopped fresh basil and a little fresh sliced Parmesan or Pecorino cheese to garnish

1 banana

Day 4

Breakfast

Luxury muesli (high in fruit and nuts) with skimmed milk, topped with chopped cantaloupe melon or mango or orange
Slice of wholemeal bread with honey

Lunch

Three-bean salad served on mixed salad leaves with a tomato, celery and onion side salad tossed in vinaigrette, served with small slice rye bread
I apple OR
Warm quinoa or bulghar wheat pilaf mixed with chopped mushrooms, canned, drained green lentils, a few caraway seeds, chopped cucumber and parsley
I apple

Evening meal

Red mullet covered with an olive sauce made by blending (in a food processor) some stoned black olives with crushed garlic, fresh basil, chopped fresh tomato and a little lime juice, and then baked in the oven until cooked through; new potatoes sliced, tossed in olive oil and seasoning, and baked; selection of green vegetables OR
Skate wing or cod fillet, baked, grilled or fried in a little butter, served with tomato salsa (deseeded fresh ripe tomato, green pepper, red onion, fresh chillies, cucumber, all diced and tossed with a few cooked chickpeas, fresh coriander, seasoning, olive oil and white wine vinegar to taste); new potatoes as above
I banana

Day 5

Breakfast

Good portion of natural bio yoghurt topped with a portion of fresh chopped fruit, including orange, with sunflower seeds and linseeds sprinkled on and a little honey.
Slice of wholemeal bread with a little spread and Marmite.

Lunch

Courgette, couscous and chicken salad (small courgettes, sliced, brushed with olive oil and grilled, tossed with lean cooked chicken pieces in vinaigrette and served with couscous soaked in chicken stock and tossed with pine nuts. OR
Egg and prawn salad (hard-boiled egg, sliced and served with cooked tiger prawns, cooked brown rice, chopped Cos lettuce, a little olive oil mayonnaise
1 apple

Evening meal

Spaghetti, cooked and served tossed with chopped fresh sage leaves, chopped spring onions, toasted pine nuts, extra-virgin olive oil, seasoning and sliced Parmesan or Pecorino cheese; side salad OR
Fresh tuna steak, lightly grilled and served with a salad of grilled red peppers, stoned black olives and anchovy fillets in vinaigrette dressing; egg thread noodles
1 banana

Day 6

Breakfast

Poached eggs on wholemeal toast, I orange or ½ grapefruit OR
Luxury muesli with orange chopped in and skimmed milk to taste,.
Slice of wholemeal toast with pure fruit spread

Lunch

Salad of grilled Halloumi slices, diced and tossed with cooked wholewheat pasta shapes, halved cherry tomatoes, pine nuts and sunflower seeds, chopped fresh mint, olive oil and lemon juice OR
Fresh hummus with pitta bread, lemon wedges and a green salad
I banana

Evening meal

Baked chicken with red onions (toss chicken breast fillets, each cut into two, red onion wedges and small chunks of parboiled potato in olive oil, season and place in shallow baking dish with unskinned cloves of garlic and bake for about 40 minutes and serve with a side salad or green vegetable OR
Moroccan marinated chicken (marinate strips of chicken breast fillet in a mixture of olive oil and lemon juice, chopped red chilli, crushed garlic, chopped mint and a little saffron for an hour or so, then fry in a non-stick pan in a little olive oil over a medium heat until cooked through); serve with couscous reconstituted in chicken stock
I apple

Day 7

Breakfast

Good bowlful of natural bio yoghurt topped with chopped apple or berry fruits and some luxury muesli, with a little honey if liked
I slice of wholemeal bread with a little spread and pure fruit spread OR
Grilled goats' cheese and berry fruits with Italian bread

Lunch

Salad of cooked flageolet beans and puy lentils, tossed with strips of grilled red pepper, chopped red chilli, fresh thyme and chopped spring onions mixed with cooled cooked quinoa or bulghar wheat, olive oil and lemon juice with seasoning to taste OR
Fresh cannellini bean and vegetable soup (e.g. New Covent Garden) with a small slice of rye bread
I banana

Evening meal

Potatoes boiled and mashed with olive oil and chopped parsley, served with poached eggs garnished with anchovy fillets; side salad OR
Cheese risotto made by sautéeing risotto rice in a little olive oil/butter with some thinly sliced leeks, fresh chopped oregano or marjoram and crushed garlic, then gradually adding hot vegetable stock, cooking until the rice is tender and creamy. Stir in soft goats' cheese to taste at the end before serving; side salad

2 If you want to feel more alive there is one simple thing you can do for almost instant, but also lifelong results – move your body ... get air into your lungs. Activity equals enhanced energy, both physical and mental.

exercise for energy

activity is the secret key to super-vitality – and it's free

How exercise energizes

If you have a sedentary lifestyle, the very idea of exercise can seem exhausting – and the idea that it can actually increase your energy levels, somewhat peculiar. However, exercise can energize you in several ways. Here's how.

Exercise and oxygen

Certain types of exercise – the kinds that fall into the category of aerobic exercise – force you to increase the amount of air that you breathe into your lungs and therefore the amount of oxygen that your body receives. As your lungs are working harder, you will also be expelling more carbon dioxide, the waste gas. This has the effect of increasing your metabolic rate by helping you to burn up fuel (calories) more quickly.

Think of your metabolism as a fire, food as the logs. Think of the air you breathe as a breeze fanning the flames of the fire and making the flames burn higher and brighter. All food needs air to convert it into body fuel. The harder and deeper you breathe, the more air you get inside you, the more your metabolism speeds up and your perceived energy levels increase – all your body functions are working more quickly.

Aerobic exercise also strengthens the lungs, increases their capacity, strengthens the heart (which is a muscle) and increases its bulk. A strong heart and healthy lungs will make you feel more alive, more energetic.

Exercise and circulation

Exercise increases the speed at which oxygenated blood circulates around the body because the heart is pumping more volume with every beat. This means that more vital blood, with its supply of oxygen and nutrients, is being carried more efficiently to all parts of the body, to every cell, to your muscles, your skin, everything – including your brain.

Increased circulation bring the body alive, it keeps the body warm. If you are in normal health and yet constantly cold it is likely that you need to improve your circulation – and the only way to do this, really, is to exercise.

Exercise and strength

Exercise of the right type – that which exercises the major muscle groups in your body – increases the proportion of lean tissue (muscle) in your body. Work your muscles with strength training (also hard aerobic exercise, such as cycling or jogging, will increase muscle strength in the used muscles) and they put on bulk. Bulkier muscles give you a stronger body, and a stronger body helps you to feel more energized – mostly by helping you to feel less tired during and after physical work.

Increasing the amount of strength-building exercise that you do also has other benefits, such as increasing bone mass and improving posture and body shape.

Exercise and health

All research shows that regular exercise undertaken at a suitable level for a suitable duration affects overall health in many positive ways. For example, it can boost the immune system, lower blood pressure, help you to relax by releasing endorphins and dispersing adrenalin, induce better sleep, help keep weight stable, minimize the symptoms of PMT and stimulate lymphatic drainage.

Sport for strength

All aerobic exercise will also offer something in the way of increased strength – usually in the leg muscles – but here is a quick guide to which sports will help which muscles.

CLIMBING: arms, back, thighs
CYCLING: legs, buttocks
ROWING: arms, chest, shoulders, abdomen
RUNNING: legs, calves, abdomen, buttocks
SKIING: legs, buttocks, abdomen
SQUASH: buttocks, legs
SWIMMING: arms, chest, back, shoulders (depending on stroke)
TENNIS: buttocks, legs
WALKING: legs, calves, abdomen, buttocks

Rest periods and common sense

Just because enough exercise is good, that doesn't mean more is better. All research shows that you need to rest for at least 24 hours after a serious exercise session in order for your body to recover. A muscle doesn't increase its bulk, for example, while you are actually exercising it but afterwards, in response to the extra work that it has been given.

Any type of exercise that asks the body to do more than it has done before needs to be followed by recovery time. If you fail to do this, you may find yourself feeling exhausted rather than energized – which is where we came in!

It is also vital to exercise at a suitable level for your current fitness. The idea is to build fitness gradually and sensibly. Go mad at something when you're unfit – e.g. you haven't taken a walk in a year and suddenly you're out there trying to climb a mountain – and you will not only suffer aches and pains, but be disinclined to try again. This applies to both strength and aerobic exercise. The rule is to push your body JUST beyond what is easy and no more.

If all of these conditions are helped or prevented, then energy levels will naturally be higher. Nothing is so draining as chronic symptoms of ill-health.

So for all these reasons, it makes sense to exercise. In the following pages you will get ideas for both aerobic and strength exercises, which will also help increase your mobility. The stretch-type exercises in Step 1 increase your flexibility further and should be combined with the exercise routines in this Step for all-round physical fitness.

Increasing your aerobic fitness is not a very hard thing to do. You simply need to get your lungs breathing in more air, and your heart working harder, for at least 20 minutes at a time, 3–4 times a week. The suggestions that follow here will help you to do that.

The walking programme

Everybody walks – at least from time to time – but very few people ever walk in such a way that they receive any true aerobic benefit from their walking. In other words, most of us just dawdle along, perhaps with the dog, stopping frequently. However, when it is done correctly, walking can be just about the best aerobic exercise there is.

For walking to be aerobic, you need to go at a good pace without stopping to admire the view or the shop-window displays; and for it actually to do your heart and lungs any good, you really need to do it for at least 20 minutes. As you get fitter, you will need to increase the time spent and/or speed or intensity in order to see continuing benefits – and this applies to any aerobic activity.

Training zone heart-rate

Write your own Training Zone heart-rate here:

VERY UNFIT PERSON	BEATS PER MINUTE
Minimum (220 minus your age x 60%)	....
Maximum (220 minus your age x 70%)	....
AVERAGE UNTRAINED PERSON	
Minimum (220 minus your age x 70%)	....
Maximum (220 minus your age x 80%)	....

Keep between your chosen minimum and maximum !

Finding your correct training zone

If you want to get technical, you can get a heart-rate monitor which you strap on to your chest and the display unit that comes with it (usually a watch) will tell you if you are working at the right level of intensity for aerobic benefit.

The right level to aim for is between 70 and 80 per cent of your maximum heart rate, MHR being 220 beats per minute minus your age. If you are extremely unfit you can begin at 60 per cent, and when you get very fit, you can train at 85 per cent.

Example: If you are 40 years old your MHR is (220 minus 40) 180

Perceived exertion scale

How does the exercise feel?

	EXERCISE LEVEL	% OF MHR	AEROBIC EFFECT
1	Very, very light		No aerobic effect
2	Very light		No aerobic effect
3	Light		No aerobic effect
4	Fairly light		No aerobic effect
5	Moderate	60%	Light training zone
6	Quite hard	70%	Suitable training zone
7	Hard	80%	for most people
8	Very hard	85%	Training zone for fit people
9	Very, very hard		No aerobic effect
10	Much too hard		No aerobic effect

and so your correct training level is between 126 (70 per cent of 180) and 144 (80 per cent of 180) beats per minute. Generally, beginners should keep their rate at the lower end, and the fitter you become, the harder you can work. If working at 70–80 per cent seems too hard for you, use 60 per cent as your minimum and 70 per cent as your maximum until you are fitter.

If you don't want to purchase a heart-rate monitor you can check your pulse-rate several times during your workout. Do this by placing the middle fingers of your right hand flat on the carotid artery on the right side of your neck underneath your jaw (it is the easiest pulse to find). To an accurate count of 10 seconds, count the pulses that you feel, then multiply by 6 to get your heartbeat rate per minute.

You can also get a very good idea of the correct intensity of your workout by using the Perceived Exertion Scale as shown at the bottom of the opposite page.

Another simple way of telling if you are working within your training zone is the 'talk test'. As you walk, can you hold a conversation? If the answer is no, then you are working too hard and should slow down until you can.

Lastly, there is the 'breath test'. As you walk, can you feel your lungs working harder than if you were at rest, breathing in more deeply than normal? If the answer is no, then you are not working hard enough and should try a bit harder until you can.

NOTE: If in doubt about your fitness or health, check with your doctor before beginning an aerobic programme of any kind.

How to walk

Now you know what you need to achieve, it's time to get walking. Wearing suitable clothing and comfortable supportive walking shoes or boots, and with a watch, plus an isotonic drink (see page 72), walk through the Time and Distance Chart below, with a minimum of 3 sessions a week and a maximum of 4. All you do is start with the time given for Level 1, and aim to walk the distance given in Level 1 in that time. At first you may not be able to walk that distance in that time – but you soon will. Then move on to the next level and aim to walk that distance in that time and so on.

Time and distance chart

Level	Distance	Time	Level	Distance	Time
1	1 mile	20 minutes	4	2 miles	30 minutes
2	2 miles	40 minutes	5	3 miles	45 minutes
3	2 miles	35 minutes	6	4 miles	55 minutes

More aerobic sport

You don't have to stick with cycling or walking. Vary your aerobic activities in the months and years to come with other sports and ideas, but match your chosen activity to your current fitness level.

IF YOU LIKE CLASSES ... think about Astanga Yoga (power yoga) or BodyPump. Enquire at your local leisure centre or gym about both.

IF YOU LIKE CIRCUIT-TRAINING ... think about short sessions of high-intensity activities, such as skipping, stair-climbing, rowing.

IF YOU WANT TO DO SOMETHING AT HOME ... consider skipping, perhaps the hardest aerobic workout of all, or rebounding (mini-trampoline) or a step platform.

IF YOU WANT EXTRA INTEREST... try orienteering (see the Appendix), mountain-biking, skiing, dancing, swimming.

IF YOU WANT TO BE COMPETITIVE ... take up cross-country running, run a marathon or join a club where you can compete once you are proficient (e.g. rowing, cycling, swimming, orienteering). Your library will have details of local clubs or try the Internet.

The walking should be on fairly level ground, otherwise the distances will be wrong – obviously, walking uphill is harder (much harder, in fact), so you will have to go slower, and walking downhill is easier, so you won't get the aerobic effect unless you virtually run! You will need to measure out your distance – the simple way is to wear a pedometer, available from sports shops, or measure the distance by car.

Later on, though, when you are fit, you can include hillwork, which will help you get fitter without having to put in lots of extra time. As you get fitter, you can, if you like, put in extra time and distance over and above that stated.

In addition to the times given in the programme, you should add on 3 minutes for warming up, walking slowly and gradually building speed, and for cooling down at the end of the programme, gradually slowing down. This is important as you don't want to push your body when it is cold; your heart-rate needs to increase gradually and this time will also help your muscles to warm up and prevent aches the next day. You should also do the leg stretches, which appear on page 89 in the Strength Programme warm-up, before and after the programme.

Walk with an even, long gait, with back straight, shoulders relaxed and down, arms swinging forward and back, stomach tucked in and heels to the ground first, followed by toes. Concentrate on breathing deeply and evenly, in through the nose, out through the mouth. For drinks, waterproofs, map, etc., use a small rucksack that fits snugly and evenly across your upper back.

Don't forget to check whether or not you are walking within your training zone several times during your walk – this is the most important part of the whole exercise. How long it takes you to reach each level doesn't matter (and if you are very unfit, you will find that it may take you weeks), as long as each time you go out walking, you stay within your training zone. Then, eventually, you'll reach the final level – it may take a lot less time than you think – and by then you will be SUPER-FIT! Indeed, if you reach Level 5 you will be more than fit enough to see the energy benefits that fitness brings and you may prefer to stop at that stage.

Note: If you begin on Level 1 and find it easy – i.e. it is not bringing your heart-rate up to a minimum of 70 per cent, then move on to Level 2, or whichever level you need to do so. This means that you are already fitter than average. You may prefer to try the Cycling Programme.

Remember: If you don't have a heart-rate monitor, check your training zone four ways – take your carotid artery pulse, use the Perceived Exertion Chart, try the Talk Test, or use the Breath Test.

Once Level 6 is attained, if you want to improve even more, aim to get your time over 4 miles down lower. Once you can do 4 miles in around 48 minutes (a speed of 5 m.p.h.) you will really need to start running to improve further. Otherwise, maintain your fitness by walking for 20 minutes, 3 times a week, covering 1.5 miles, with regular longer walks when you feel like it.

The cycling programme

For fitter people, cycling is an excellent aerobic activity. Most of the notes that I've written for the walking programme also apply here so READ THEM FIRST. Also, you must make sure that your bicycle is roadworthy and that you remember the Highway Code and wear a protective helmet. Cycling on busy roads – or, indeed, on country lanes – can be dangerous, so TAKE CARE.

Note: Times assume fairly level roads. Try to pick a route that is level, especially when you're a beginner. Slogging up hills in a low gear and then coasting down them isn't the way to get fit. Aim to cycle in a medium-high gear throughout.

Time and distance chart

Level	Distance	Time	Level	Distance	Time
1	3 miles	20 minutes	4	6 miles	24 minutes
2	6 miles	40 minutes	5	9 miles	30 minutes
3	6 miles	30 minutes	6	12 miles	40 minutes

The strength programme

As well as conferring all the many benefits listed on pages 81–3, strengthening your major muscle groups is also necessary in order for you to carry out your aerobic exercise properly. If your muscles are weak, they won't be able to carry out enough work to provide your lungs and heart with the workout they need!

To increase your body strength you need to work all the major muscles of your body with resistance. This means either using your own body weight as resistance (as in exercises such as press-ups and dips), or using free weights, such as dumbbells, or resistance items such as stretch tubing. Alternatively, of course, you can visit the gym and use their state-of-the-art resistance equipment. The programme here uses body weight and optional free weights to help you gain muscle strength. As a plus, your body shape and tone will also improve.

Instructions

- You should do the programme 3 times a week, evenly spaced out. Most people prefer to do their strength programme on alternate days to the aerobic programme but, if you prefer, you can do them on the same day.
- You should also do the warm-up and cool-down as specified in the next few pages, to help prevent muscle aches, pains and injury. Whenever appropriate, some of the exercise moves have an inset box describing a more advanced version of the exercise, for when you have improved. Save these until you find the intermediate version too easy.
- From start to finish, including warm-up and cool-down, the routine should take about 20 minutes – perhaps a bit more at first until you get familiar with the moves.
- Stretches should be held for 10 seconds in warm-up; 20 seconds in cool-down.
- Each exercise should be performed slowly and in a controlled way, and the move repeated 12 times for one set. Add on more sets as you improve. To build strength you need to do repeats/sets until the working muscle(s) begin(s) to feel tired and possibly start to shake. If you don't work to this point, you won't improve.
- If using free weights, start with the lightest – 1kg each – and work up as you improve. If you don't use weights for exercises in which they are recommended, improvement will be much slower. If you want to work with weights but don't want to buy a set, you can use food cans or filled mineral water bottles as a substitute.
- Wear comfortable unrestrictive clothing and non-slip training shoes.
- Don't exercise shortly after a meal.

Warm-up

1 March on the spot, swinging your arms, for 3 minutes, gradually lifting your knees higher until the thighs come up parallel with the floor and gradually swinging your arms higher. Breathe deeply throughout.

2 Shrug your shoulders up and down a few times and do 12 large arm circles with both arms to the back, and then to the front.

3 STRETCH YOUR CALVES. Stand as shown with one leg in front of you and the other out behind you, arms outstretched to a wall, with the leg to the front straight and the heel firmly into the floor. Feel the stretch up the back of the calf in the rear leg. Repeat with the other leg.

4 STRETCH YOUR QUADS (thigh muscles). Lie on your side as shown, gripping your foot around the lace area to bring your heel in towards the buttock. Hold for a count of 10. Release and repeat to the other side.

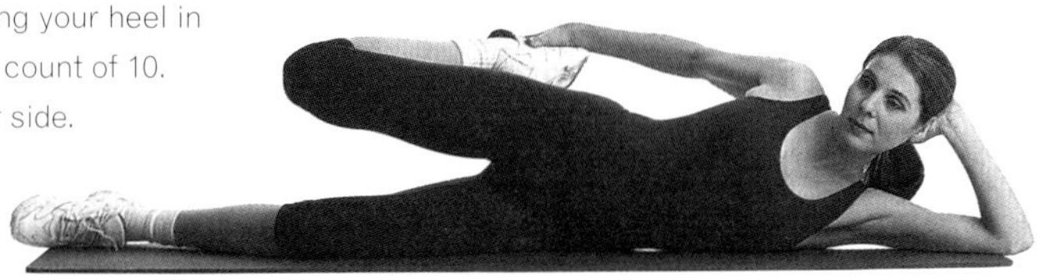

5 STRETCH YOUR HAMSTRINGS. Sit as shown, with one leg bent, the other straight out in front of you. Move the body forward towards the foot of the straight leg (let the movement come from the lower back), with the hands leading (use a hand towel around the foot, if necessary) and, when you feel a strong stretch in the hamstring of the straight leg (behind the thigh), stop and hold the stretch for a count of 10. Repeat to the other side. As your hamstrings become less tight, you will be able to reach further down your leg and eventually grasp the toes of the straight leg easily.

At this point you can also do short versions of all the other stretches mentioned in the cool-down, if you like, which will help your muscles to relax further – a good idea if you are particularly stiff, cold or inflexible

- Use a mat for all exercises

The routine

1 CHEST AND ARMS: Kneel on all fours with your palms flat on the floor, arms straight, fingers facing forwards. Take the knees backwards. Bend elbows and, not allowing the back to sag, dip towards the floor until your forehead is an inch or two above the mat. Slowly raise to the starting position and repeat 12 times for one set.

Chest and arms harder version

Start with your legs straight and lower body weight on your feet, the hips slightly lifted and arms as shown.

Dip towards the floor as in basic move, slowly raise and repeat.

2 LOWER BACK STRENGTHENER: Now lie on your stomach on the mat, with your hands resting on your buttocks, palms upwards. Keeping your hips and legs firmly into the floor, raise the upper body off the floor a few inches (or as far as you can go, this may be only as little as an inch or so at first), sliding your hands down your buttocks as you do so. Don't try to look up. Slowly lower your body to the floor and repeat the process 12 times for one set (or as many repeats as you can, if it is less than this – this exercise is much harder than it looks).

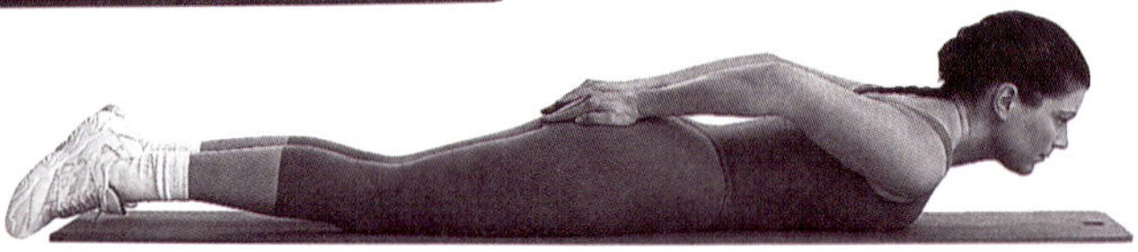

3 BICEP (FOREARM) STRENGTHENER: Now stand with your weights (lightest to start with), one in each hand with palms facing upward, knees 'soft' and stomach and buttocks tucked in, elbows neatly tucked in to the waist. Slowly raise the weights to the front of your shoulders as shown, slowly lower and repeat 12 times for one set.Increase the weights as soon as you are able.

4 LATERAL ARM RAISES FOR SHOULDER DEFINITION: Take the same standing position, but this time hold the weights in either hand by your sides, palms inwards. Now slowly lift the arms up and out until they are parallel with the floor, slowly return to the starting position and repeat 12 times for one set. Increase the weights as soon as you are able.

5 TRICEP (BACK OF ARMS) DIPS: Sit on the edge of a sturdy chair with your hands on either side, fingers facing forward over the edge. Lower the buttocks off the chair and dip down until the elbows are at 90 degrees as shown. Pull up and repeat (without sitting back on the seat) 12 times for one set .

6 HAMSTRING (BACK OF THIGH) CURLS: Now kneel on all fours, with back strong. Lift one leg until the thigh is parallel with the floor, and then slowly curl the lower leg in towards the buttock, squeezing in as far as you can before returning to the parallel position. Repeat 12 times, then repeat with the other leg for one set.

7 LUNGES: This exercise strengthens the whole leg. Stand with feet hip-width apart, arms by your sides, stomach tucked in and back neutral, shoulders relaxed. Take a big step forward with one leg, until your thigh is parallel with the floor, letting the other leg bend so that knee dips towards the floor (but doesn't touch it). Come back to the starting position and repeat with the other leg. Repeat on each leg 12 times for one set.

Lunges harder version

If you like, you can hold weights in both hands while you do this exercise and each time you come forward on to the leading leg, do a bicep curl (see exercise 3). Strap-on ankle weights will also make this exercise slightly harder.

8 WIDE-LEG SQUATS: (for thighs, hips, buttock) When squatting, always keep your back as upright as you can, stomach tucked in and don't let the thighs dip below parallel to the floor to avoid knee strain. Stand with feet wide apart and in line with the legs, and arms in front of the chest as shown. Now slowly squat down, bending at the knees as low as you can go without tipping forward too much, until the thighs are parallel with floor (you probably won't be able to go that far at first). Slowly return to the starting position and repeat 12 times for one set.

Squats harder version

When you have come down into the squat position, raise yourself on to your toes to work the calves. Return the feet to the floor, then return to standing position and repeat the whole move 12 times. You can also include lateral arm raises with this move later (with or without weights), see exercise 4.

9 ABDOMINAL CRUNCHES: Lie on the mat with the knees bent, feet flat on floor and hands resting either side of temples. Have only a slight gap between the small of the back and the floor. Think about your stomach muscles. Now on an out breath, raise your head and neck off the floor, using the abdominals to pull you up. Slowly return to the starting position and repeat 12 times for one set.

Abdominal crunches harder version

From the same starting position but with arms by your sides, bring the legs, still bent, up into the air and cross the ankles. Now, raise arms, head, neck and buttocks off the floor and curl into yourself. This works the lower abdominals. Slowly lower and repeat 12 times for one set.

10 DIAGONAL ABDOMINALS: To work the muscles at the sides of your waist and across the abdomen, lie on a mat as in exercise 9 but with the left arm outstretched to the side. Now aim your right elbow towards your left knee (keeping the right arm back, though, rather than bringing the elbow forward), then slowly lower. Keep the left arm on the floor throughout. Repeat 12 times, then repeat to the other side 12 times for one set.

Cool-down stretches

1 HAMSTRING STRETCH: Repeat the Sitting Hamstring Stretch as described in the warm-up (page 89), holding the stretch for 40 seconds in each leg.

2 TRICEPS STRETCH: Still sitting, (in a chair if you prefer), raise the right arm and place the right palm on the upper back. Now press the right elbow backwards, using the left hand, until you feel the stretch up the right triceps and shoulder. Hold for 15 seconds, then repeat to the other side.

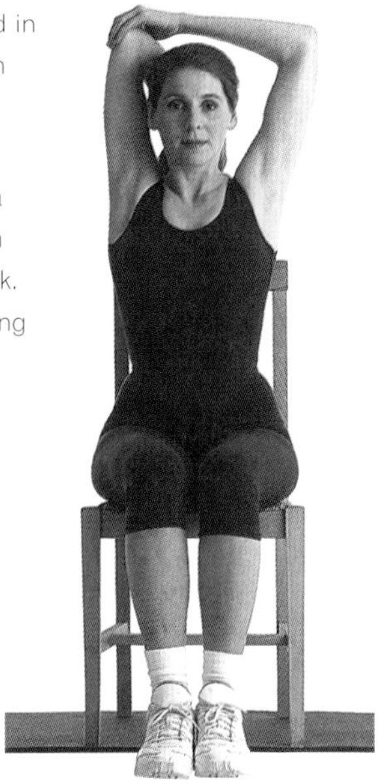

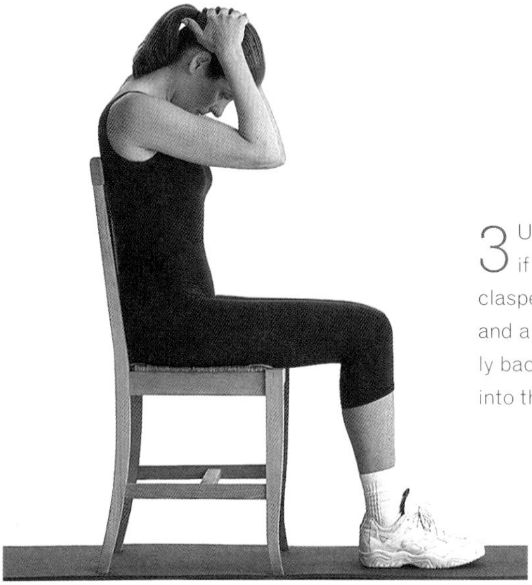

3 UPPER SPINE STRETCH: Still sitting (in a chair if you prefer), place the hands with fingers lightly clasped across the back of the head just above neck and allow your head to drop forward. Then lean slightly backwards until you feel a stretch up the spine and into the upper back and neck. Hold for 15–30 seconds

4 QUAD STRETCH: Lie on your side and do the Quad Stretch as described in the warm-up (page 89), holding on each leg for 15–20 seconds.

5 LYING CALF STRETCH: Lie on your back and raise the right leg into your body and then up into the air. Now flex your right toes as hard as you can to feel the stretch in your right calf. Hold for 15–20 seconds, lower and repeat with the left leg.

Strength tools

As we've seen, you can exercise to build strength using nothing more than your own body weight and some 'weights' from the larder. You may, however, like to consider buying one or two 'tools' to help you – some of the most useful items are the cheapest.

RESISTANCE TUBES / BANDS: These are basically long stretchy bands or tubes, with a hand-hold at either end, which offer resistance and can be used in many exercises from bicep curls to rowing. They come in different resistances, so they will suit both beginner and advanced, and usually come with an exercise wallchart. They are ideal for travelling with as they are light and small. They only cost about £10 per set.

ABDOMINIZER: A tubular contraption with a padded headrest to help make stomach exercises easier on the head and neck and to help your posture while doing them. Basic models are around £20, up to £80. They help make the dreaded abdominals a little less like hard work!

ANKLE AND WRIST WEIGHTS: These strap on to ankles/wrists with velcro or similar and add weight to any exercise and to cardio work. Ankle weights are particularly useful as obviously your feet can't hold ordinary dumbbells! They are less bulky than traditional weights.

A note about more expensive gym-type equipment for the home: Don't buy really cheap stuff as it won't offer enough progression and may fall apart or be unstable, or take too long to set up/put away. Go for the absolute best you can afford and consider carefully where you are going to keep it.

6 LOWER BACK, HIP AND BUTTOCKS STRETCH: Still on your back, bring the left leg in towards your body and, grasping the leg with both hands around the thigh, gently pull the knee in towards the chest until you feel a stretch in the lower back, left hip and left buttock. Hold for 15–20 seconds, then repeat to the other side.

7 LONG BODY STRETCH: Do the Body Stretch as described on page 37. This will stretch out your abdomen, chest, front of shoulders, biceps and spine. Hold for as long as you like. Get up slowly.

2 Getting older doesn't necessarily mean an inevitable decrease in physical energy? With a few simple measures it is possible to retain much of the vitality of youth Here we look at ways to maintain optimum energy well into old age.

age and energy

the ageing process can be slowed right down

What exactly is the ageing process?

The ageing process is generally perceived to include the gradual decline of energy levels, an effect that some people notice as young as their thirties, while others carry on with as much stamina and vitality as ever well into their retirement. The difference between the two is probably down to a variety of factors: genetic predisposition, mental attitude, an enjoyable lifestyle, and attention to diet, exercise and looking after yourself. Your genes can't be altered, but virtually everything else can. Let's look at the main ways that ageing affects the body and what you can do about it.

Muscle bulk decreases.

In people who do no strength training, muscle is lost at about 5 lb (2.25 kg) in weight for every ten years after the twenties. At 50 you could then have 10 lb (4.5 kg) less muscle than you did at 30. With muscle loss, obviously strength, stamina and energy decrease and, because muscle is more metabolically active than other body tissue, metabolic rate decreases too. However, with regular exercise, most of your muscle mass can be retained into old age. Use it or lose it!

Bone loss

Bone mass can begin to deteriorate, on average, at around the age of 35, and we lose about 0.5 to 1 per cent a year. For women, this loss then accelerates to about 5 per cent during, and in the years after, the menopause. Loss of bone causes further decrease in metabolic rate, increased risk of fracture, frailty and skeleton shrinkage.

Strength exercise, adequate calcium intake throughout life and, for women, hormone replacement therapy (HRT) during the menopause can conserve bone mass – and the earlier regular exercise is begun, the better. It is also important to maintain a reasonable body weight in adulthood as thinness predisposes you to osteoporosis in later life.

Slowing of the metabolic rate

It is estimated that, on average, the metabolic rate (the rate at which our bodies use energy) slows down by about 20 per cent between the ages of 30 and 70. This is not only caused by loss of muscle and skeletal mass, but also by a range of other factors – the weight of our brains, our livers and other organs decreases, the speed at which our bodies carry out the various autonomous functions decreases, lung capacity decreases by a tremendous 60 per cent at 70 compared with age 25, and resting heart rate declines too – IF we do nothing about it.

Little research has been done on what factors influence conservation of brain and liver mass and other organs, but lung capacity and heart-rate – both of which have an undisputed effect on energy levels – can be maintained with regular aerobic exercise.

Cell production slows down

When we are young, all the cells in our body replace themselves, but as we grow older production of new cells can't keep up with the death of old ones – which results in what we call the ageing process. One cause of this is the production of free radicals which, over time, can cause alteration and damage to cells.

It is the free radical process which, experts believe, also causes much of the illnesses of old age, such as heart disease and cancer. The long-term damage (or malfunctioning) of cells and our body systems as we get older is probably responsible for various health problems associated with middle- to old-age, such as arthritis, diabetes, thyroid problems, and degeneration of eyesight, hearing, taste, appetite, and so on. If you think of the ageing process as the body battling to fight off these effects, it is no wonder that often older people complain of feeling tired and lacking in energy.

And think about

As you get older, you may have more disposable income to spend on what you may have once considered indulgent luxuries. Have you ever:

- Been for a holiday to a health farm?
- Had a course of body massage?
- Tried reflexology – a diagnostic aid as well as a treat?
- Tried shiatsu (acupressure) to help release energy and relax you?
- Had a session with a personal trainer?

See the Appendix for addresses.

Our main defence against the free radicals and their effects is a diet high in antioxidants, which, in effect, 'mop them up' (see page 66). Such a diet contains high amounts of foods rich in vitamins C, E and the mineral selenium, and fresh fruits and vegetables.

In women, there may be a loss of energy at or around the menopause, including increased tiredness, muscle weakness, lack of mental stamina, loss of memory and lack of libido. Research suggests that HRT can reverse or prevent these symptoms. Natural hormones can produce mild effects similar to HRT without any possible negative side-effects, and these can be found in a range of foods, including yams, soya beans, nuts, linseeds, pulses and wholegrains.

Six ways to keep old age and low energy at bay

You can't stop the ageing process completely, and you can't expect to feel quite as energetic at 80 as you did at 18 – but there is plenty you can do to slow down its progress.

1 EXERCISE Almost all the signs of getting older can be minimized with exercise, done sensibly and regularly – but not to excess. Ironically, if you over-exercise, more free radicals will be produced.

2 EAT A GOOD DIET If you're young now, DO start eating a healthy diet as laid out in this book IMMEDIATELY. The sooner you start, the more benefit you will reap, both now and later in life. You need plenty of fresh, wholesome foods with a wide variety of fruits, vegetables, grains, nuts, seeds, pulses, fish and plant oils. This will increase your intake of not only the vital nutrients like calcium and iron, but also important antioxidants.

3 DON'T SMOKE AND DON'T DRINK ALCOHOL TO EXCESS Both increase the production of free radicals.

4 KEEP A REASONABLE BODY WEIGHT Not too thin, not too fat. Obesity 'slows you down' and increases the likelihood of various health problems in old age – e.g. heart disease, diabetes and arthritis.

5 KEEP POSITIVE You need to keep your brain in the right frame of mind, so that you are motivated to keep your body in good health. If you enjoy life, you are much more likely to want to live in a body that works for you. For more on this see Steps 3 and 4.

6 HAVE REGULAR CHECK-UPS Get yourself a thorough body check-up at least once a year – heart, blood pressure, cholesterol and so on. The earlier problems are spotted, the easier they are to treat and the less damage they will do to you and your energy levels.

Step 2 round-up

AT THE END OF STEP 2 YOU ARE – PERHAPS FOR THE FIRST TIME IN YEARS, IF EVER – IN TUNE WITH WHAT YOUR BODY NEEDS IN ORDER TO GIVE YOU TOTAL ENERGY.

• You now know what your body needs in terms of fuel, exercise, maintenance, time, thought and effort. For most of us, a lot of work is needed to bring our bodies 'up to scratch' – the longer you've been neglecting those walls, that structure, the longer it WILL take ... but you will get there. You've made the right start.

• You should now feel stronger, more positive, more alive, more confident that you can make of your body what you want it to be.

• You have spent two steps 'inside yourself', thinking of YOU. At the end of Step 2, I would now like you to begin to think about the world around you, because in the final two steps you are going to think about how you and your energy levels relate to the outside world.

• I would like you to feel ready to tackle the life problems that have been sapping your energy, and to feel ready to solve them and make order, balance and harmony out of chaos.

• Whether it is work, home life, relationships, your own irrational fears or worries – you can sort them out and release yourself from the negativity that is holding your energy back.

Now say:

I can be in control of my own life.

....and move on to Step 3

step 3

Controlling the Chaos

Managing your life and your emotions to conserve and create energy

If physical energy is equivalent to a car's engine and fuel consumption, think of mental energy as all the controls of the car. Immediately you can see that it is easy to cause damage by 'bad driving'. The human equivalents of hard braking, unnecessary acceleration, poor gear-changing and so on are things such as unproductive thought, lack of planning, badly handled situations and confrontations, non-ideal relationships and negative emotions. A high percentage of your potential energy can be wasted every day on these chaotic influences.

Step 3 is where we train your brain to manage your energy correctly and smoothly. We want to create harmony and efficiency in order to decrease stress, conserve the energy you have, and create even more. We want to minimize chaos and maximize order. That way you will achieve more time, more peace and more control. Mental energy, like physical energy, is not just something some people have by luck – it can be found by everyone.

In Step 3 you will find out what your own most chaotic areas are by doing the questionnaire on the following pages. Then we will discuss better time management, beginning with a look at the fascinating area of body rhythms and your own personal body clock.

Your surroundings have a big influence on your energy levels . With this in mind, we find out how you can improve your home, your workplace and even your car, so that you feel both more serene and more energized.

We look at mental stamina... How do some people keep going for longer than you? How can you do it too? And we look at managing your emotions... How you can deal with life in a positive way rather than waiting for all it chooses to throw at you? Whether they are caused by you or by others, fear, anxiety, worry – we turn these negative, enervating emotions into something positive and energizing and show how you can choose to be happy!

Remember that in the building that is total energy, Step 3 is the control centre, the core of the building, the key to your optimum energy.

Control the chaos – and increase your energy by at least 25 per cent. Now it's time to begin.

Week 3

General notes:
Don't forget to continue with your Aerobic and Strength exercise programmes, as well as your Eating for Energy programme, and build in some regular massage, stretch and relaxation time. As you get fitter, think of including different aerobic exercise instead of just the walking (e.g. the cycling programme on page 87, or see the list on page 86).

Day 1
- Read through Step 3.
- Do the Surrounded by Chaos? questionnaire overleaf.

Day 2
- Look at the way you manage your time and think about your own body clock, with the help of pages 107–9.
- Think of as many ways as possible to streamline your life.
- Start writing 'to do' lists every evening.

Day 3
- Check out your surroundings with the help of the advice given on pages 116-19.
- What can you do to improve the ambience of your home? De-clutter? Redecorate? Move things around? Write out a list of improvements you can make and aim to schedule them into your life.

Day 4
- Now look at your working environment. What can you do to improve it too? (see pages 121–2)
- Think about doing some regular desk exercises at work (see the suggestions on page 121).
- Find some ways to improve the quality of your travel time (see page 122).
- Read the section on training your brain (see pages 125–7). Try the stamina exercises. Aim to improve.

Day 5

- Following the ideas on pages 128–31, see what you can do to improve your relationships.

Day 6

- Consider your stress levels at work (see pages 132–7).
- Read about 'situation stress' (see page 134) and see what you can do to minimize its effects in your life today.

Day 7

- Do the quiz about happiness on page 138.
- How is your happiness rating? If low, start a Mood Diary (see page 140) and see what you can do to change this.
- Read Step 3 round-up (see page 141).

TURN THE PAGE TO START STEP THREE

Surrounded by chaos?

Do the quiz here to discover how much your chaotic lifestyle is affecting your energy levels. Circle the answer to each question which is nearest to how you behave in that situation, then check overleaf for your scores and total them up.

1 Ahead of you is an even busier week than usual and you don't know how you will cope. Do you:

a *Go through your diary and see what you can delegate/cancel without causing more problems?*

b *Get through the week as best you can, feeling fraught?*

c *Phone in sick and let others sort it all out?*

2 Your energy levels in both mind and body fluctuate during the day in your own particular pattern. Do you:

a *Go with your body's rhythms and make the most of them?*

b *Override them, believing in the strength of your own will-power?*

c *Disagree with this idea – you've never even thought about it?*

3 A boring but very necessary and quite urgent task features on your agenda. Are you likely to:

a *Reckon you'll do it when all the other, less boring, tasks are done?*

b *Throw a tantrum so that everyone feels guilty/sorry for you and you can get out of it?*

c *Decide to do it straight away and save the nicer/easier chores until later?*

4 How much time do you spend organizing your daily life?

a *A lot – everything I do is pre-planned.*

b *Very little – other people in my life do all that for me.*

c *Hardly any – I prefer to see what the day brings.*

5 Your partner has lost his/her job, or you haven't been picked as Chair of the committee you were banking on organizing. Do you:

a *Plot revenge?*

b *Accept that disappointments are part of life, and move on?*

c *Fight the people who made these decisions and try to get them altered?*

6 Your job has really been getting you down for some time now and you know you are worth more. Do you:
a *Stick it out anyway because you really dislike change and don't want to worry your dependants by resigning?*
b *Stay fuming inside, until one day you'll blow your top and get fired?*
c *Think about and talk through what you want to do instead, then set about doing it, even if it may take a while?*

7 Thinking far ahead now – do you have a plan for what you want to achieve in your life?
a *Yes – but I never do anything without consulting my astrologer and my biorhythm charts.*
b *I have a complete life plan and so far it's working out well.*
c *Life's a lottery, so there's little point in planning too far ahead.*

8 Which most closely sums up your view of your current relationship (whether full-time partner or just dating)?
a *Sparky – lots of rows but exciting and passionate.*
b *Compatible but dull – maybe someone better will come along.*
c *My partner enriches my life and I am sure this relationship will last.*

9 Think about your main daily surroundings (e.g. home, workplace). How do you feel about them?
a *I never really notice my surroundings.*
b *They are just as I want them.*
c *Awful, but haven't the time/money/authority to alter them.*

10 How would you sum up the whole picture of your life now?
a *Relaxed and balanced well between work, home, family and social life.*
b *Unbalanced – all or nearly all of one thing, none or little of the rest.*
c *Orderly – everything and everyone has their allotted time and no more.*

Add up your scores:

1. a 5 b 1 c 3	6. a 1 b 3 c 5
2. a 1 b 5 c 3	7. a 3 b 5 c 1
3. a 3 b 1 c 5	8. a 1 b 3 c 5
4. a 5 b 3 c 1	9. a 3 b 5 c 1
5. a 1 b 5 c 3	10. a 3 b 1 c 5

Your total score is ....

What your score means

40–50: You are great at conserving energy because you are organized, careful, thoughtful and cautious and you absolutely hate wasting time or not knowing where you stand. Watch out, however, as you can be a bit too fond of control, perhaps a bit too intolerant – and if it all goes wrong, as occasionally it is bound to do, your stress levels will rocket and your well-ordered life can collapse. You should also learn that sometimes it is good to let go and relax. Are you SURE your organized life is as stress-free as you think it is? Also, a highly ordered life can sometimes be boring, and therefore enervating. Lastly, watch out that you don't become too self-centred... feedback from others is energizing.

25–39: To others you often seem relaxed, laid back... and you do feel in harmony with life, at least some of the time. However, your energy levels may fluctuate from quite good to poor. You tend not to spend enough time on yourself, your body and your feelings. You also tend to make spur of the moment decisions or rely on others to decide for you, either of which can land you in energy-draining situations – if not today, then at some time in the future You need to face your problems more. Then your feelings of guilt, anxiety and being slightly 'out of control' – all of which are never far beneath the surface – will fade and you will truly be as relaxed and energized as you seem.

Under 25: Was the Chaos Theory invented for you? You are certainly surrounded by chaos. In small doses, this can be exciting, refreshing and therefore energizing. More often, however, and certainly long-term, it is de-energizing, because you waste more energy than you create. Looking busy, running round in circles, isn't the same as getting things done. Try to bring some order into your life, to save both time and energy – otherwise exhaustion, both mental and physical, will never be far away. There are plenty of ideas for you in Step 3. Take at least some of them on board, get more control of your life and you'll find those unexplained bouts of panic disappearing before long.

3

Whenever you waste time, you also waste your energy. These pages are designed to help you use your time more efficiently and therefore to conserve – indeed create – maximum energy.

managing your time

clever use of your time will help save both physical and mental energy

Going with the flow – your body clock examined

For maximum energy, you need to be in tune with your own body rhythms, by which we are all, to a certain extent, governed. Ignore these rhythms and you face unnecessary stress and fatigue. Go with them and you have the beginnings of perfect harmony – and energy conservation and creation.

The main factor dominating our body clock is the 24-hour circadian cycle – night and day, light and dark. Over millions of years, humans have evolved to sleep when it's dark and wake with the light – a sensible system for a species that can't see in the dark.

These two most important cycles – and all of our body clock rhythms – are controlled by neurons called the suprachiasmatic nuclei, mostly based in the hypothalamus area of the brain.

During sleep, these SCNs cause most main body functions to lower – heart rate, lung function, urine production, temperature, blood pressure – by regulating the balance of hormones and body chemicals. As daylight approaches, they increase the production of others to stimulate wakefulness and the daytime rhythm begins.

Within the day, there are various recognized patterns of 'mini' cycles, each of which will affect the way that you feel – your energy levels, your different cognitive functions and so on.

For most efficient functioning, it is important to recognize these cycles and 'go with them' rather than trying to fight them. If you try to override the signals that your brain receives from the SCNs you will undoubtedly feel under par.

Let's take as an example one of the more obvious functions controlled by the hypothalamus: you are in the gym exercising and you begin to feel thirsty. The hypothalamus has recognized the need for water and has literally converted that need from the unconscious level into your conscious thought so that you feel the drive to drink. If you choose to ignore that drive, you will continue to feel thirsty and eventually you will dehydrate.

In a similar way, ignoring the less obvious, but equally important, body rhythms can result in both physical and mental impairment.

Below we look at a typical day, with the most likely cycles for most people, and offer tips on how best to deal with them. Overleaf we discuss what to do if your rhythms don't seem to match up to this average. Obviously there will be times and days when you can't follow the guidelines exactly, but for smooth running of both body and brain, it is worth trying at least most of the time to fit your schedule and your lifestyle in with your natural body rhythms.

Your body clock

12–4 a.m.

This is when most of our deep restful sleep occurs – vital for repairing and refreshing the body and brain. If you suffer from fatigue, a busy lifestyle or stress, try at least to make sure that you have the opportunity of sleeping during these hours.

4 a.m.

Around 4 a.m. blood pressure and body temperature are at a low. Between then and 6.00 a.m., if you have to work either physically or mentally, your ability to concentrate or work hard will be impaired. This is also the time when the highest percentage of people die.

6 a.m.

Towards morning, REM 'dream' sleep increases and the brain gets more active. However, REM sleep occurs throughout the night and if you are particularly wakeful around 6 a.m. it may be your natural time to get up rather than worrying about staying asleep until the alarm goes off. Also, the SCNs are beginning to activate the hormone cortisol, which, like adrenalin, is a 'fight or flight' hormone and will help you feel more awake. Meanwhile, levels of the night-time hormone melatonin, which helps us to sleep, are dipping.

8–9 a.m.

This is the most likely time for people to suffer a heart attack or stroke – probably because the body is suddenly being asked to 'perform' after several hours' inactivity, coupled with the rise in adrenalin. If there is any suggestion of your having cardiovascular problems or you are a 'high risk' person, this is the time to wind yourself up slowly, NOT get out of bed to do 100 sit-ups or a run, but warming up the body gently and trying to remain relaxed.

The body also begins to send signals that it needs feeding after the night's fast – breakfast is an important meal (see Step 2).

9–12 a.m.

This is the time when the brain is at its most alert, and we are most able to do hard mental tasks, talk most lucidly and communicate well with rapid responses. Programme your important meetings and phone calls for this time, as well as using these hours to solve problems and do written work.

12–2 p.m.

Here the brain remains on good form and you may find it useful to take a late lunch-break and work through until 2 p.m..

2–5 p.m.

Big lunch or not, you may find your performance dips now – though research shows that a heavy lunch will impair performance further. Use this time to do tasks requiring less effort and concentration. Manual dexterity may, however, begin to improve and so this will be a good time to perform light physical tasks. Your heart-rate and blood pressure are slowly beginning to lower.

5–6 p.m.

The heart and circulatory system are working at their optimum efficiently now. Your muscles will also be warm and less likely to strain. After an afternoon in the office, this is a very good time to exercise – a gym work-out or an aerobic walk, for example. Walking home from work will also be much less of a chore than walking to work in the morning.

6–8 p.m.

In summer, mental alertness should have another 'mini-peak'. In winter, however, when it is dark the SCNs will be beginning to secrete the sleep hormone melatonin and you will begin to feel mentally and physically more relaxed and perhaps tired. This is the best time to drink alcohol, when it is well tolerated because your liver, which processes the alcohol, is at its most efficient.

10.30–11.30 p.m.

This is the best time to go to bed. Melatonin levels are very high and you should be fast asleep by midnight and enjoying the deep sleep that will prepare you for tomorrow.

How average is your body clock?

Various factors – perhaps including frequent travel through time zones, shift work and genetic make-up – may give you a body clock rhythm that doesn't fit the typical pattern. Some people, for instance, come awake late at night and prefer to sleep until noon, or find that their brains are at their slowest on arrival in the office at 9 a.m., and most active around 5p.m. when it's time to go home. If these different patterns cause you no problems, then they don't matter – just monitor your body clock for a few days and use the comments on the list above at the different times for you.

If you would prefer to conform, however, research shows that you can alter your body clock. For instance, if you want to change from being a 'lie-in' expert to an early bird, it may take only a week to re-set your body clock. You simply need to set an alarm clock at the same early time every morning until you find that you are waking up just before it goes off.

You then get straight out of bed. Do this every morning for another week and your body clock will be re-set. Of course, you will also need to go to bed earlier in order to compensate.

Monthly biorhythms

The idea that we each have three different internal biorhythms governing physical, emotional and intellectual capacity began around 100 years ago. It is said that these cycles can be charted monthly and vary according to our date of birth. When each biorhythm line crosses a horizontal line on the chart these are said to be 'critical days' for that particular cycle. Some people plan things such as important meetings, holidays, risky operations and so on according to when their biorhythm charts tell them that the time is right.

Some studies suggest their is evidence that monthly biorhythms exist, but most of this evidence is anecdotal only, and recent research has been inconclusive at best, negative at worst. Some people feel that they may work like the other unproven 'science', astrology, for people lacking in enough confidence to trust their own instincts and judgement – I.e. if you get your personal chart done and use it to plan your life, you will feel more in control and therefore your life may, indeed, improve.

Planning and streamlining

Recent research has found that we spend, on average, 2½ years of our lives wasting time. You can save lots of time and energy by pre-planning and streamlining – at home as well as at work.

It is estimated that most people waste considerable amounts of time every day simply by being disorganized. This is in addition to time wasted on pastimes that may be neither pleasurable nor necessary – e.g. watching TV programmes out of habit.

Time wastage equals energy wastage, so these pages are designed to help you use your time more effectively and therefore conserve and create energy.

Planning

It is surprising how many of us wake up most mornings with very little idea of how we intend to spend the day ahead. The main prerequisite of good time usage is that you actually think about what you want to achieve beforehand. So, at the end of every day, with pen and paper in hand (or the computer, electronic diary, or whatever), ask yourself, 'What am I going to do tomorrow?' This will achieve various positive benefits: it acts as a memory aid, so you can sleep easy knowing that posting that birthday card won't be forgotten; and it makes you organize yourself – with a structure to the day, you are less likely to be distracted into time-wasting, by others or by yourself, and you will be more motivated to do whatever is on the list.

Dividing your 'to do' list up into categories, according to your own life, also helps. Most people will find a list for home (chores, family, chauffeuring, etc) and one for work is helpful. You should also have a personal list for 'You' things, which we will discuss in more detail in Step 4. The home list can be pinned on a notice-board in the kitchen or hallway and the work list put in your briefcase/bag or on your desk at work. As you write your list, cross-reference with your diary so that you include any appointments, anniversaries, etc.

The next thing to decide is when the items on your list are going to be done. Some things you won't be able to alter – appointments and so on. Others you can do in the most streamlined fashion possible. Don't forget to think about your body clock (see previous pages) when planning your day and most people find that it is more efficient – and easier – to get hard or unliked chores out of the way as early in the day as possible, otherwise they tend to hang around in your brain and may make you irritable, worried or even depressed, each of which drain energy.

Lastly, assign each item on the list a time for completion. This makes it more likely that you will complete it on time.

At the end of each day get into the habit of making up a new list, including anything on the previous list that didn't get done, as a priority for tomorrow.

It will also help you plan if you check your diary regularly for what will be coming up in the weeks – and even months – ahead, so that you don't end up with last-minute panics over promised reports or 20 cakes to make for the school fête and only one evening to do them in. Your daily list should almost always include some work or effort or planning towards these longer-term commitments. However, beware the trap of putting so much on your list that you're never going to have time to get through it all. That is the way towards feeling guilty and frustrated – two negative emotions that don't encourage energy, but drain it. BE REALISTIC! If you've regularly got too much to do, see 'streamlining', below.

People unused to making lists may feel that the time it takes to think about and make them must be longer than the time they save. This, I can assure you, is not the case. When you get into the swing of it, your daily list will take only minutes and will definitely save you hours of time and tons of hassle.

By the way, don't feel too guilty if sometimes there is hardly anything (nothing, even!) on your list of 'to dos'. That may well mean you are running efficiently, totally in control and ahead of the game. In that case, enjoy your days of freedom and fill them with 'You' things, as explained in Step 4.

To sum up, your daily list should be in the form of a running order for the day, with a time allotted for each item. It may help you if you buy a page-to-a-day diary and use the diary itself to write your list – however, you obviously then won't be able to pin it to a wall unless you copy it.

Streamlining

Now let's look at all the other ways you can improve your efficiency both at home and at work.

- Ask yourself what is truly necessary. List or no list, you may be the type of person who takes on too much without stopping to consider why. If you are constantly running round in circles, with never a minute to yourself and only ever one small step away from exhaustion, you need to think deeply about the reasons for this. Perhaps it is lack of self-confidence (which often underlies an obsessive need to please others) or it could be because keeping busy prevents you from facing underlying problems in your life. For more help in these areas, see Managing your Emotions (pages 128–40). If you feel that you are genuinely that busy and everything you do IS necessary, read on.
- You constantly find that certain items on your 'to do' list haven't been done at the end of the day – or the end of the week. You

obviously don't want to do those items! Making an awkward phone call, perhaps, or writing a letter to an old friend, or catching up on your in-tray at work. It could be that the phone call is no longer necessary, that deep down you realize you've moved on from your old friend and no longer have anything in common. It could even be that most of what is in your in tray can be happily chucked in the bin and no one will care. Look at the things you find hard to begin tackling and see if you can find the bigger picture.

• What can you delegate? At home or at work, it is often possible to save yourself a high percentage of your own time by killing the guilt you may feel at asking someone else to 'do it instead'. If guilt – or the worry that you won't be seen as lovable if you ask for assistance – isn't your problem, then maybe you are a control freak and think no job will be done properly unless you do it. Nonsense. Anyway, if you are the boss and you can't trust your employees, you picked the wrong employees.

Get the kids to do the washing-up and some of the housework. Get your partner to do some shopping. Get the secretary who chats on the phone while you work to clear up the filing.

• What can you do in tandem? You may be able to save time by doing more than one thing at once. Try mixing a physical task with a mental one – e.g. cooking an easy meal on 'automatic pilot' while reading the paper, or ironing while using a dictaphone.

• Don't waste time waiting. Cut down on queuing times by doing whatever the queue is waiting for at a non-busy time – e.g. shop at the supermarket very early in the morning. Plan ahead so that you never have to queue to buy a travel ticket. Better still, get your tickets via the Internet. If you're forced to wait – e.g. someone is late for a meeting – be well prepared. Use the time to catch up on reading or make some useful phone calls.

• Be brutal and terminate unproductive meetings, phone calls, conversations, etc. I estimate at least 50 per cent of the time spent in business meetings is wasted in idle chat (yes, you need to exchange pleasantries, but how much?) or going over ground that's already been covered. This also applies to your private life, at least some of the time. I know that part of life is the art of small talk, but if you are genuinely busy and faced with, say, a gossiping neighbour or a relative who wants to moan on the phone when you've heard it all before, have a stock of instant get-outs ready to hand. Remember, when time is at a premium, stick to the point, and when the point has been discussed and agreed, terminate the conversation.

Also, have your intuition honed for when people ring you seemingly for a chat but actually because they want a favour. Nothing is more annoying that half an hour of idle chat with an acquaintance who, just as they are about to take their leave, says, 'Oh, by the way, can I ask you a favour?'

• Complete tasks within their allotted time. If you've designated a certain time for a chore (see page 111), stick to it. It is better to complete a task fairly well or very well in the right time than to complete it perfectly very late, or not at all, or to the detriment of all the other things you have to do. Practise this. The section on mental stamina (see pages 123–7) will help you improve your concentration, speed and brain power, etc.

If you consistently underestimate the amount of time things will actually take you to do, then allow extra time when writing your lists and put less on your list for each day to compensate. We can't all be speed kings and trying to cope with too much if you are simply not able to will only increase your stress levels and lower your energy.

• Balance your day. You will achieve more in less time if your day has a good balance between types of activity. So, if you can plan your workload to suit yourself, make sure no day consists of one only type of chore. So, if there are 1,000 daffodil bulbs to be planted and a huge pile of papers to be filed, do a bit of both each day until both are completed. Intersperse the mammoth tasks like these with smaller tasks too. And try to mix and match mental work with physical work.

If a chore is boring, try to find ways to make it less boring to help you get through it more quickly. Can you play music while you do it? Watch a good video?

Again, don't forget to consider your body clock when balancing out your day – get a routine going for daily chores/events/activities that suits your own clock.

• Get some pleasure into your day. You need order and routine for maximum efficiency, but too much order and routine can work against you. If they bring on boredom, you will become less efficient and begin wasting time (daydreaming, staring into space, etc.), so you need to have several short, and one or two longer, 'You' periods throughout the day – times when you do something you really enjoy, even if,,sometimes, this is simply doing nothing at all. Try, though, to make sure at least one or two of these 'You' periods really are fun. You need to laugh, to smile, to switch your brain to a different gear. Don't feel guilty – that is completely not the point. It'll save you time in the end. For more on the pleasure principle, see Step 4.

The rest of Step 3 will also help you to manage your time and energy more efficiently.

Don't waste time or energy on ...

Inevitabilities

If something is beyond your control and inevitable, don't waste your time or energy on trying to alter it OR on feeling aggrieved about it. Even if you do all you can for a smooth and trouble-free life, things WILL go wrong. For example, it is inevitable that occasionally your schedule will be disrupted by outside forces – there will be a fire scare at work, people will be late for meetings, you will get 'flu, the train won't stop at your station, the plane will be delayed 10 hours. It is also inevitable that time will be lost as a result of what can only be called 'Sod's Law' – the day of your important presentation you lose your house keys or your wallet gets stolen or even your home burgled. You've heard of the Chaos Theory – you can control the chaos up to a point, and that is what this step is all about, but never 100 per cent. You can do a lot towards minimizing its effects by forethought – for example, if you eat a healthy diet and exercise, you minimize your chances of getting flu, and if you leave a spare set of house keys with a neighbour, that's sensible. But silly, annoying, time-wasting, frustrating, pointless things do happen. Accept that, and when things go wrong, try to stay calm (the relaxation and breathing techniques you learnt in Step 1 will help), deal with the consequences of the situation as best you can, and then move on.

Information input overload

It is easy to fall into the trap of receiving so much information from various sources (Internet, e-mail, post, phone, fax, newspapers, etc.) that you just can't handle it all. You then feel inefficient and/or guilty and energy levels decrease. Cancel or switch off everything that isn't strictly necessary. You will feel much better for it.

Unproductive thought

Thinking is good. We all need to spend a lot of time thinking, as this is the only way we get ideas that help us steer our chosen course every day, clarify ambitions and find ways to achieve them. Thinking also helps us understand ourselves and how we relate to others. Daydreaming is good, because that is just another form of thinking. However, if you find your thinking time is taken up with negative thoughts, such as chewing over bad things that have happened in the past, or worrying about what may never happen in the future, you are wasting time on unproductive thought. With practice, you can turn this around and indulge in only good creative, productive thought. This subject is discussed in more detail in the section on Managing Your Emotions (pages 128–40) and Think Time is discussed in Step 4 on pages 155–6.

3

Most of us pay far too little attention to our environment, yet from home decor to the ambience at work and while travelling it has an enormous effect upon our well-being and total energy.

managing your surroundings

learn to function efficiently in surroundings that enhance your energy levels

Your environment – everything from seemingly inanimate objects, such as furniture, to the air that you breathe and the colours that surround you – has a profound effect upon your energy levels. You need to learn to function efficiently in surroundings that enhance them.

The ideas discussed here are taken from a wide range of tried and tested principles – Eastern concepts such as Feng Shui, colour therapy from the West, ecology, psychology, light therapy and much more. Feng Shui alone is a huge subject devoted to understanding ways of maximizing your energy potential through the energies of the cosmos; if you would like to learn more about this fascinating subject, see the Appendix.

Your home – making it work for you

Your home, whatever its size and value, should be your sanctuary, giving you your core strength and energy to 'go out and face the world'. It is your personal space and should harmonize with your personality, as well as helping to counterbalance any negative traits and boost your positive ones. For example, the right home environment can lift your mood if you are prone to depression, and/or calm you down if you often feel anxious or hyperactive. The questionnaires in this book have shown you how to establish your own personality type. Now use that knowledge to make the most of the tips here.

General ambience

When you come home, are you glad to get inside the door? Do you find the entrance – mile-long drive or communal lobby – pleasing? Does the place feel like home? If not, try to analyse why, and then find ways of making it better. (If you don't feel good at home because of other people rather than the place itself, then read the section on relationships in Managing Your Emotions on page 128.

Redecorating

This can be relatively inexpensive and achieve near-miracles, especially in creating good moods for each room. Go for stimulating colours in the dining area and kitchen, relaxing colours in the bedroom and bathroom and warming colours in the sitting area. In general, dark, gloomy hues are best avoided: brown, grey and black can be depressing. All small, dark areas – particularly the entrance hall – should be lightened and brightened with white, off-white or a pastel or something vibrant like lemon yellow. (See Colours With a Purpose on page 120 for further help.)

Lighting

Few people consider the lighting in their home sufficiently – it is often too stark or too gloomy, badly placed or simply inadequate. Nothing but a single bulb hanging from the centre of each room is depressing as well as stark. Wall lights, table lamps, standard lamps and uplighters, all create a warmer atmosphere, and a spotlight shining on where you sit and read or write will concentrate your energy. Kitchens generally need stronger light than other rooms. Candlelight is excellent for relaxation. An automatic light outside your door will improve your mood when you come home. A walk around a lighting store or browsing through a catalogue will give you more ideas than I have room for here.

Natural light in the home is vital for health and energy. If possible when moving, always choose a home with plenty of light – large south-facing windows are ideal. If you tend to have trouble waking and feel slightly depressed in the morning, pick a home where the bedroom window faces east to catch the morning sun and enhance your mood. If you get fatigued and depressed in the evening, pick a home where the sitting room/patio/conservatory faces west to catch the evening sun and improve your mood.

Homes on low ground surrounded by hills, or by tall trees, deplete energy and are conducive to depression, for the same reason that many people suffer from SAD (seasonal affective disorder) in the winter. If your home is dark, it's important to get outside regularly. If that isn't possible, consider investing in a light therapy box which mimics natural light – you sit in front of it for a short period every day and light-deprivation depression is lifted and energy restored.

Considering clutter

Some people love clutter – piles of books and magazines, hundreds of ornaments and no surface left bare, things on the floor, not an inch of wall space left without adornment. If you live that way and it pleases you, then it will energize you. However, many people who 'de-clutter' their homes find it does improve their energy levels – by clearing their minds, and creating a smooth and efficient home atmosphere, with fewer possessions to worry about.

If you're not sure, de-clutter one room first. Remove and give away, sell or throw away all unnecessary objects and effects, including wall items, ornaments and books you'll never read. Go through cupboards and drawers and do the same. If you've got dozens of dusty old half-dead house plants, they will have to go too. Remove all fussy and frilly materials (ornate curtains can be replaced quite cheaply with muslin or calico, and chairs covered with plain throws if you can't afford new ones). When you reach the bedroom or dressing room, chuck out all clothes that you haven't worn for 18 months, all toiletries and cosmetics you haven't used for 6 months. And so on. In general, if there are items you want to keep but which are still on view after your de-cluttering is finished, consider a new cupboard in which to put them. Apply similar principles to the kitchen – if you hate waste, charity shops or jumble sales may want your old saucepans or knives.

Redecorating may help complete the de-cluttering, and you can continue with the garden. Simple lines and architectural plants may bring you peace – and less back-breaking work, incidentally!

If de-cluttering your home makes you feel liberated and vital, you can always apply the same principles to the car and workplace.

Balance and harmony

Arranging your furniture according to basic Feng Shui principles will help you to feel better. When you sit down, you need a strong 'tortoise' behind you. A chair with a strong/high back, set in front of a wall, is best – avoid stools (no tortoise) and chairs positioned with open space or a door behind them, which make you feel less secure. You also need a good 'phoenix' in front of you – a clear and open space with a view. No phoenix means blockage of energy flow.

Your bed should also be in a position so that when you lie in it you have a strong tortoise (vital for restful sleep). A phoenix to look out on when you wake up would also be good.

Feng Shui also encourages round and oval objects and shapes in the home, around which energy can flow in a balanced way, rather than sharp corners, points and angles. Every home has corners or areas which don't look quite right – these can always be balanced or, at least, improved. One large plant in an empty corner, for instance (one big plant is always better than lots of little ones), or a well-placed mirror in a small area, or a rounded lamp (left switched on) in a dark recess. Rooms that seem stagnant may be improved with a water feature or moving light (e.g. a lava lamp) to create energy. Water and light can also both be relaxing.

A good Feng Shui book or, if you can afford it, a personal Feng Shui expert, who will use your birth date and other details to give you more detailed recommendations, can help improve the general atmosphere and energy flow in your home (see the Appendix).

Fresh air and water

The atmosphere in your home may be less than ideal – clinical ecologists believe that many modern ills, including fatigue, headaches and depression, may be caused by pollution. Homes near busy roads, for example, or factories, power sources and so on, may be polluted with toxins and opening the window 'to let in the fresh air' in that case may be the worst thing you can do. On the other hand, homes where fresh air can't circulate will also produce a build-up of toxins, from breathing, household products, computers, electrical appliances and so on, and not provide enough oxygen to energize the body and mind. Research also seems to be proving that mobile phones are among the worst culprits.

One simple solution is to place a few large house plants around the home. These 'cleanse' the environment, improving the quality of the air, reducing airborne pollutants and even 'soaking up' noise. Good plants for this purpose are the Spider Plant (*Chlorophytum comosum*), the Parlour Palm (*Chamaedorea elegans*), fig (*Ficus*), and most palms and bamboos. Luckily, all of these are also good to look at and not too expensive to purchase. The larger you can afford, the better, and place them near to likely areas of high pollution.

Other solutions are to purchase ionizers to clear the atmosphere and help create energy; and to keep the home as clean as you can – vacuuming regularly to remove dust, house mites, etc.

The quality of your drinking water is important too. A water filter will help remove a large percentage of the toxins it may contain.

Personal space

The majority of us live with other people, be they family or flat-sharers. In that case, it is vital for your energy that you create your very own personal space within the home – a refuge into which the other household members don't venture unless invited. This may be a room of your own, but even an area of a room is enough to give you that feeling of having your own space. Make it energizing and pleasing to you by using all the ideas above, and ensure that you have your own identity strongly stamped on it. Ideally it should be a mix of relaxation and energy (if you have the whole home to yourself, you will have different areas for different times and needs).

Colours with a purpose

Use the power of colours to enhance your mood and energy. In both your home and workplace decor you have a chance for long-term colour therapy, and in what you wear you can choose colours according to your short-term moods and needs.

Red
Promotes energy by increasing pulse rate and brain activity, and enhances your sense of power. Good for helping you through a difficult challenge. Ideal on days when you feel fatigued. Less good when you lack confidence, as it will bring more attention.

Yellow
Promotes energy and lifts depression. Research shows people feel noticeably happier in yellow surroundings. A good colour for the workplace, as it is said to improve judgement, logic and reasoning, and increase concentration and memory.
NOTE: All colour shades between red and yellow – e.g. orange, peach – have a warming and energizing effect.

Blue
Relaxing and cooling. Ideal on days when you feel tense, anxious and irritable, or are prone to bad temper. A good colour for a house which tends to be too hot. Reddish-blues and purples may be calming and stimulating at the same time – good for energy levels.

Green
Calming and relaxing, good for harmony and balance. An ideal long-term colour for the home, especially in sitting and sleeping areas. This is why you may fall asleep outdoors on a summer day – it isn't just the warmth, it is the total greenness surrounding you!

White
Calming, soothing and good to help clear confusion and restore clarity. May also be cooling. A good basic colour for the home, especially the dark home, and wearing white clothes in winter can lift depression. Pink seems to have a similar effect to white.

Black
This – and all other dark colours, such as slate-grey, dark brown, dark navy – are best avoided, except in small doses, if you tend to lethargy and/or depression.

Neutrals
Beiges, stones and mid-browns – the neutrals – are calming but can be depressing if used too much, bringing a lack of focus and energy. They are ideal if used to balance highly energizing colours such as red. In home decoration, energize a neutral room with a few 'hot' cushions, for example.

Your workplace – making it good for you

Many of us spend as long in our place of work as we do at home, if not longer. The workplace is where our energy levels really need to be high, our concentration good and our motivation strong. Therefore it makes sense to use what we know to improve our work environment to the point where it actually helps us to be more efficient and productive.

Most of the tips given for improving the home will also apply to the office. The lighting is important, as is the decor. The furniture – especially if you're a sedentary worker – is critical. Your chair and desk need to be supportive, comfortable, and with a good tortoise for security and phoenix for inspiration and energy (see the principles of Feng Shui, pages 118–9). The air quality should be good – lack of oxygen is a common cause of fatigue and energy slump at work. Plants and/or an ionizer can remedy poor air quality. Piles of filing need to be removed from view and clutter minimized.

You should also have a designated relaxation area for regular break times, and make sure to get out of the building in which you work at least once during the day, if only to see daylight. Being shut in with nothing but artificial light all day is a cause of depression and low productivity.

Desk exercises

Your working day can be enhanced if you spend 2–3 minutes every hour doing a few loosening/relaxing/energizing exercises that can all be done sitting in your chair, or standing.

- Sit with shoulders as relaxed as you can manage, hands on lap. Shrug tops of shoulders up as high as you can go, and down as low as you can go. Repeat 12 times.
- Place palms of hands across back of your skull just above neck. Exert gentle pressure to bring the chin down towards your chest. Feel the stretch in the back of the neck. Hold for a count of 10.
- Slump forward in the chair with arms hanging loosely down. This eases a tight lower back.
- Sit with your elbows on the arms of a chair, forearms raised slightly. Let your wrists and fingers go floppy and circle each hand clockwise then anticlockwise 10 times. This will help avoid strain, particularly if you spend long hours at a keyboard or working with your hands.
- While sitting, march on the spot, bringing your knees up a few inches in turn, flexing the feet to feel a slight stretch in the calves as you do so. This will help your circulation.
- Stand up and walk around at least once an hour, and, if possible, go up and down a flight of stairs. Again, this helps circulation and concentration.

Of course, all this may be easier for me to advise than for you to put into practice, unless you happen to be the boss. However, any organization with any sense, realising that a happy workforce equals more productivity and therefore more profit, will be happy to listen to suggestions on how to improve the working surroundings and atmosphere. So don't be afraid to ask for changes. You will often get what you want. If you don't – consider moving elsewhere.

Travelling – making it better for you

After home and work, many of us spend our next largest chunk of time travelling. If you are a regular commuter you will know how frustrating and stress-inducing it can be. Here are some tips to help minimize the negative effects.

By car

• Make sure your car interior is clean and de-cluttered. Make sure the car is regularly serviced and that it is a car you like and find easy to drive.
• Have relaxing music for traffic-jams and other frustration, and stimulating music for boring motorway-type drives to help keep you energized.
• Have good air-conditioning; an overheated car in summer will drain energy. Keep the temperature slightly cool all year round.

By public transport

• Remember the tortoise and phoenix principle – sit with a strong back (ideally, nobody behind you) and open phoenix. Face the way you are travelling and sit near a window.
• If you have to stand, stand looking out of a window with your back against a wall. Move your feet frequently to avoid pooling blood.

For all commuter travelling, by whatever means, remember the rule about inevitabilities that we discussed in the last section. Delays and frustrations WILL happen, so at these times try to remain stoical and accept the situation rather than allowing your temper/blood pressure/anxiety to rise. Deep breathing and something absorbing to read or listen to will always help.

Relaxation versus stimulation

• Work out which are your lowest-energy times and places. These are the ones which need stimulation.

• Work out the worst high-stress/anxiety times and places. These will benefit from relaxation techniques.

3 You may be losing a huge amount of your potential energy by not using your brain power most efficiently. Here we look at ways of improving both your mental concentration and your stamina.

managing your mental stamina

how to turn a butterfly brain into an efficient energy-conserving powerhouse

Many people waste a great deal of energy in 'pussyfooting' around problems, in avoiding boring tasks or in allowing themselves to be distracted from the important issues in their lives. Here we look at ideas that can help convert a 'butterfly brain' and conserve energy.

By using psychological training and physical techniques, your brain, like your body, can be taught to perform better and keep going longer. With good mental stamina, you can improve the amount and quality of your work and reduce the time spent in working or problem solving, giving you more time and space to relax and enjoy life.

Physical considerations

Your brain consists of physical matter, just like the rest of the body, and it follows that it needs good treatment in order to give peak performance. All the areas considered in Steps 1 and 2 – diet, exercise, rest and sleep – as well as good general health, are factors in keeping your brain in trim.

Good diet

You've heard the expression 'brain food' – and it's true that some things really are. Here they are explained:

Glucose Without a steady supply of glucose, which arrives via the circulation of the blood, your brain won't function properly. Glucose is its source of energy and, like any other part of the body, energy is its fuel. Food that we eat is converted into glucose, and the best type of food for the brain is slow-release complex carbohydrate with a low glycaemic index. If you've forgotten what that is, turn back to page 70. It is these types of foods – such as whole grains, pulses and so on – that keep the blood glucose levels most constant and which, therefore, provide a constant stream of energy for the brain. Foods high on the glycaemic index will provide you with a quick 'shot' of glucose, but the dip that follows will not be worth it.

This is why it is vital for brain power that you eat a low-GI, well-balanced breakfast after the night's fast, and the ideal way to eat for the brain throughout the day is several small meals or snacks – I recommend three small to medium-sized meals at regular intervals and two small snacks in between, all containing some foods low on the glycaemic index and none consisting of nothing but high-GI foods. So, for example, good brain snacks would include a handful of brazil nuts, a slice of dark rye bread with low fat spread and Marmite, an apple and a piece of lean ham, a handful of sunflower seeds and an orange.

Long-term, your brain also needs plenty of antioxidants, and more research is showing that a diet high in the essential fatty acids – found in plants, nuts, seeds and fish – helps smooth brain functioning. A diet high in saturated fat may have a detrimental effect because arteries leading to the brain can become 'furred', just like those coming from the heart – and furred arteries reduce efficiency considerably. Refer back to the diet section for more advice on all of these.

Lastly, research shows that brain power and alertness decrease, and fatigue and lethargy increase, after a meal that is unbalanced, containing too much carbohydrate, particularly of the refined type (white pasta, bread, puddings). This is another reason why meals should be 'little and often' and why lunch should contain moderate amounts of complex, low-GI carbohydrate along with protein, which helps to keep the brain alert. The only time of day when you can afford a high carbohydrate meal is in the evening, when you may want to slow brain function down before bed.

Coffee Research shows moderate amounts of coffee during the day can improve concentration and alertness. About 4 cups a day is the optimum amount – much more than that and negative effects may begin to show.

Supplements Both gingko biloba and ginseng supplements have been shown to aid brain function, in the case of gingko by increasing blood circulation to the brain. Ginseng's action is less clear, but it does seem to work for some people.

Exercise

In order to work well, your brain needs not only glucose but also a constant supply of blood and oxygen via the circulation. The best way to achieve this is to exercise regularly and keep yourself fit as described in Step 2, so that the circulation is most efficient. Research shows that older men who keep fit and exercise aerobically regularly have brain function on average as good as men 20 years younger.

Sleep and rest

All research shows that people deprived of sleep have seriously impaired brain function, particularly in terms of short-term memory and reaction time. Logic, concentration and reasoning have also been shown to suffer. So follow the advice for sleep on pages 44–51. Regular rest periods during the day are also beneficial – I don't necessarily mean literally having a nap, but little breaks every hour or 90 minutes, when you do something completely different for 2 or 3 minutes, help to refresh the brain.

A strong body

If you are healthy, balanced and strong, with a good immune system, your brain is likely to work better than if you are weak, poorly and generally below par. The agility and stamina of the brain tend to decline with age, but all research shows that a brain that is used regularly, and stretched, retains its faculties for much longer than one that is under-used; and, in general, a fit person suffers less from loss of intellect than an unfit person. The message is clear – body power equals brain power or, at least, the basis for it.

Training your brain

How can you fight off brain fatigue and keep going to the very last word of that long report, or concentrate all the way through a marathon 8-hour seminar, when you have to write the minutes? Use these tips...

Concentration

This is the ability to focus on the matter in hand, keep your mind totally on it and not wander. It is a vital skill to nurture. Losing concentration during an important lecture, for instance, may mean that the rest of it doesn't make sense. Losing concentration frequently during the working day may mean that by the evening you haven't finished the work that you should have sailed through in the time. Failing can result in nothing but frustration and drained energy levels. Here are some simple things that may make a difference...

Setting time limits Decide beforehand how long a task should take you and aim to complete it in the allotted time. This should focus your mind sufficiently, especially if you have something you want to do after the time limit is up. For example, say you have a paper to read which you reckon should take an hour, plan to go and get your hair cut when you've finished.

Motivation It is always easier to keep concentration as long as necessary if you have a compelling reason to do so. For instance, a busy project equals more money in the bank for you, which equals that longed-for holiday in New Zealand. So you concentrate until the project is done. Every time you have a task to complete which requires concentration, think of your own motivation. If there isn't one and if, in fact, there rarely is one, it could be that your lifestyle is to blame rather than your concentration levels. Step 4, then, may hold the key.

Interest The fact is that if you do things that you find interesting, concentration is rarely a problem, because, as we've just seen, you are motivated by your interest in them. If bored, concentration levels will naturally dip. Try to find ways to improve the interest level in what you have to do. Again, if you can't, see Step 4.

Meditation Meditation, as described in Step 1, is a good tool for practising concentration, because it is true that basic concentration can be improved with practice. Focus in on yourself, or on an object or word, and meditate for a few minutes – building up to 30 minutes – regularly until you can focus on your chosen thing throughout the allotted time without anything else breaking through. Apply this to tasks which require concentration.

Short bursts If your concentration over long periods of boring tasks is poor, you can, as we've seen, lose a lot of time during the day. However, if you control short periods 'off' every hour or so, in which you say, positively, 'I am going to spend the next 3 minutes reading a magazine,' or 'I am going to walk round the block now,' you may find your concentration improves after these mini-breaks because you have made a conscious decision about when they are going to begin and when they are going to end. This is akin to the 'rest breaks' mentioned on the previous page.

Conscious effort Sometimes it is important that your mind really does stay in focus on something until it has finished – the lecture, for example. You can train yourself to keep concentrating. Every time your mind wanders off, make a conscious effort to pull it back where it is supposed to be. Say to your brain, 'You are going to go back now to the lecturer and listen carefully. You are not interested in that wallpaper over there.' Another way to keep concentrating in such situations is to take notes.

Speed

Many of us find that we work much more slowly than we'd really like. There are several ways to increase the speed at which you can complete tasks.

Reading It is relatively easy to increase the speed at which you read. With practice, you can double it. First you need to increase your concentration. Before you begin to read anything – newspaper article, phone listings, book – put all other thoughts out of your brain. Now begin reading, skimming more quickly than is normal through the lines. At the end of the page, what did you understand of what you read? Write down whatever you can remember of what you have read. You will find that you did take in some of it.

The more you do this 'skim reading', the more you will take in, until eventually you can read every word more quickly than you ever believed. But it does take concentration. Focus!

If you don't believe you will manage to do this, take a test. Think of the name of a local pub. Now get your telephone directory or Yellow Pages pub listings and skim down the columns at the rate of no slower than 3 seconds a column, concentrating as hard as you can on picking out your chosen pub name as you go. I bet that you spot the pub even while skimming three times as fast as you'd normally run down a listings directory. Think of other things or people to look up and see how much quicker you get with practice.

Tasks The last good idea to increase the speed of what you do is, again, to set time limits. You have heard of Parkinson's Law, which is that a task will expand to fill the time you have available. In the same way, most tasks will contract to fill a shorter time.

The importance of balance

Remember that, in general, if your day is balanced, with a range of different activities and tasks, some physical, some mental, then both your physical and mental stamina should increase. You can keep working at your maximum for longer and longer, with practice, but everyone needs variety in the day. Put in a 16-hour day today, working on the same thing, and tomorrow your brain can be forgiven for saying, 'No thanks, I've had enough.'

3 Negative emotions, such as fear, jealousy, boredom, resentment and loneliness, can easily enter our lives and even dominate them – yet they are all energy-draining if allowed to continue for too long.

managing your emotions

coping with the negative feelings that may enter our lives and drain our energy

Many people are led by their emotions, and their days are shaped by how they feel at any given time. Often these emotions are negative, and negative emotion is highly draining of energy. So here we look at how to manage these emotions – and cope with the situations in which you are most likely to find that they appear.

Negative emotions are all forms of stress, or are, at least, stress-inducing. Not all stress, however, is negative. Short-term stress can be positive, having a beneficial effect on your health and your energy. Stress – particularly the kind that makes you feel more alive (e.g. pre-performance nerves), not the kind that makes you feel less alive (e.g. depression, boredom) – increases the flow of adrenalin and other stimulating hormones and also increases your heart-rate, and thus will temporarily increase energy. This type of stress, experienced for short periods, is good and can actually boost the immune system and make you more able to cope with crises.

Stress begins to be negative and energy-draining when it becomes long-term or dominant. Here we look at ways to minimize the negative energy-robbing emotions that may be taking over.

Relationships

Relationships are vital in most people's lives and can be a potent source of energy. Sex, for example, is energizing and people with a good and regular sex life have been shown to live longer, be healthier and be happier than those without. Communication and interaction are stimulating and energizing, and no one would deny that an evening spent talking and laughing with people you care about is a tonic that is hard to beat. Yet relationships are also the prime cause of chronic stress and negative emotions. Marriage and love partnerships all too often bring jealousy, suspicion, lies, resentment, misunderstandings, anger, fear, depression and almost all other emotions known to man and woman!

Some stress in any relationship is normal and desirable, and may be energizing. For example, anger that leads to an argument that is satisfactorily resolved is 'good stress'. However, unresolved negatives – unaired grievances and long-term problems – will create depression, and are a constant and debilitating drain on your energy resources.

You can begin to improve your skill at creating energy-enhancing relationships in several ways.

Try to pick people who energize you A simple but excellent piece of advice for anyone looking for a partner, this tenet also applies to friendships and even working relationships. Choose people who make you feel good! We can all think of a person who, when we see them, within minutes or even less, our spirits sink and we feel depressed. We can think of others who give us a real buzz and can change our mood from down to up in seconds when we see them.

Yes, people can change – when you live with them, for instance – but this is as good a starting point as any. Hopefully, you will have the same effect upon them in return.

Keep your sense of self Don't let a relationship take you over and, in particular, don't let the other person engulf or dominate you. Make sure you keep a life of your own – try to carry on making your own decisions at least some of the time, do what you want to do at least some of the time. Keep your self-esteem strong.

Keep talking If you don't talk about things that are bothering you within a relationship it is highly unlikely that they will be resolved. It's vital to have a partner you can talk to about how you feel and what is happening in your lives. Get used to airing problems before they become mega-grievances.

Keep trying Keeping a relationship good is a lot easier than mending it once it's broken. And many of the problems in love relationships are NOT to do with love or sex or infidelity, or even money, but simply involve poor 'human relations' – i.e. you just don't deal with each other in a warm, humanitarian way. Taking each other for granted is a sure way to build up negative emotions

Relationship counselling

You may know a relationship is making you unhappy, but you may not be sure why, or how, to resolve it. In that case, professional counselling may be a good idea. If you are married or living with a partner, you can go to Relate, an organization with years of experience in dealing with partnership problems – you can go alone or with your partner. See the Appendix for the address.

on both sides. Do you do these things for your partner?

• Keep a look-out for signs that they are suffering negative emotions of their own (worry, overwork, etc.)

• Always have one ear open – and time – to listen to what they have to say to you.

• Try to say positive, warm, light and cheerful things more often than you moan, groan, nag or complain about life in general.

• Show affection (other than as a prelude to sex).

• Cope with their occasional mistakes and faults without blowing your top.

If you do all these at least most of the time, you can expect them to do the same for you. See also the section In Pursuit of Happiness on page 138, which explains how you can often 'turn round' a less than great relationship simply by practising positivity every day.

Aloneness

Perhaps you are not in a love relationship and/or you have trouble forming or maintaining relationships of any kind, or feel that you don't want to. Such a situation is not all negative – energy levels may be enhanced by the increase in the freedom to do as you choose. There is certainly a great sense of release to be had in freeing yourself from enervating friendships, hangers-on and so on. Many people live alone and wouldn't have it any other way, and anyone who has always been surrounded by people should take at least one block of time every now and then to be alone – take a holiday alone, stay at home alone, whatever – to get a taste of how it feels. Change is almost always energizing.

However, it is important not to enjoy your own company so much that you miss out on regular human contact. Books, music, etc. may provide 'company', but real energizing stimulation comes from being with other people, talking, exchanging ideas, laughing and so on.

Lack of stimulation drains energy, creates lethargy and is to be avoided. For more on that subject, see Step 4. By the way, shyness is, in my opinion, merely a lack of practice in human contact. Feel the fear and do it anyway! For more on that philosophy, see page 134, where we discuss 'situation stress' and how to deal with it.

If you lack friends, relationships and contact, and would like to change that situation, here are some ideas.

- Join a club specializing in something you enjoy. Friendships are much more easily made when you have a common interest.
- Change your workplace to somewhere where there are more people.
- Join a singles club, where there are regular events organized, e.g. Drawing Down the Moon (see the Appendix).
- Get out of your home and travel – if you can't face doing it alone, go with a company that specializes in group holidays for singles. Walking or hobby holidays are ideal.
- Offer your talents and services to a local charitable organization whose work appeals to you.

Eating to avoid stress

We've all heard of comfort eating and the phrase has negative connotations – get upset, binge on chocolate, put on weight and get even more upset! However, there are ways to eat that really will help to minimize periods of stress.

Carbohydrates are relaxing – it's official. Foods such as bread, potatoes, pasta, bananas and cereals help to relax you when you are stressed-up by encouraging the production of the 'feel good' chemical serotonin in the brain. That is probably why we binge on 'carbs' when upset. For best health, go for complex carbohydrates (see the diet section in Step 2) rather than refined carbs, which, as we saw in the section on Mental Stamina, will make you feel lethargic.

Magnesium and calcium Eat more magnesium and calcium. These two minerals work to help calm the brain and can induce a better night's sleep – vital if you are stressed. Rich sources of magnesium are nuts, dried fruits, whole grains, pulses, leafy greens; and rich sources of calcium are low-fat dairy products, fish, dark leafy greens.

B group vitamins Vitamins from the B group are essential stress-busters. They can improve mood and reduce anxiety levels. They're water-soluble and needed in the diet every day – and stress, smoking, and alcohol can all 'use up' more vitamin B in the body. Eat whole grains, nuts, meat, fish, milk and pulses.

Alcohol Avoid more than 1 glass of alcohol a day, as alcohol is a depressant and reduces performance – which, in itself, is stress-inducing.

Coffee Avoid more than 4 cups of medium-strength coffee a day – in moderation, coffee can improve performance, but overloading can worsen stress.

Beating overwork stress

If you try to do too much, of course then you will feel drained of energy and you will feel stressed. What is too much for you may not be too much for someone else, and vice versa – and it is possible to train yourself, as described on the previous pages, to do more by careful time management and brain training. You cannot go beyond a certain limit, however, without feeling the full force of negative stress and fatigue. The box below will help you to decide whether or not you are suffering from overwork-related stress.

Ways to deal with overwork

As we saw earlier, some forms of stress can be positive – and occasional bouts of overwork may be fine for you. The key is to allow your body and brain recovery periods of enough frequency and duration. If you need, or like, to work hard (and that includes all kinds of work, not just your official 'job'), follow this plan:

- Set a schedule for the day, decide what time you are going to finish work and stick to it.
- Plan into each day a short break at least every 2 hours, including a longer break halfway through the day. Do something different during your short break – read, listen to music, go for a walk, shut your eyes, do some exercise (see box opposite).
- Allow yourself one full day of recovery for every three days of hard work that you do. This doesn't necessarily mean a day off work, but a day with easier tasks, a day with shorter hours, less stressful events, with little, if any, hard 'brain work'.
- Have at least one day a week truly 'off' – relaxing and doing something you enjoy, perhaps nothing at all.

But what happens if you don't like to work hard and yet you feel that you HAVE to? Many people, often called 'breadwinners', carry on working beyond their natural boundaries for fear of letting their dependants down, or for fear of being out of work if they don't. Sometimes the dependants or the boss simply don't realize the

Symptoms of overwork stress

- Insomnia, including not being able to get off to sleep and waking in the middle of the night, brain racing.
- Overuse of tobacco, alcohol, coffee, perhaps prescription drugs or recreational drugs.
- Constant feeling of being under pressure.
- Resentment.
- Chronic tiredness.
- Concentration powers diminished; memory poor.
- Tasks you usually, or used to, find easy become hard.
- Inability to relax.

Pilates for stress relief at work

Re-energize yourself regularly throughout the day by doing some simple exercises and stretches based on the principles of Pilates. You can also try those described on page 121.

Breathe correctly Sit with spine strong, shoulders relaxed, hands in your lap. Breathe in slowly through your nose and down your chest, until your whole rib-cage is expanded. Slowly breathe out through your mouth. The increased intake of oxygen will help you remain alert while the slow deeper breathing will help reduce your blood pressure and heart rate and help you to relax.

Posture check Remove your shoes if possible (in fact, it is useful, if you are a sedentary worker, for you to wear no shoes or flat slipper-type shoes throughout your working day), so you can sit with heels and toes flat on floor. Sit with your lower back firmly to the back of the chair, tummy tucked in. Lengthen your spine and relax your shoulders until your head naturally sits balanced well on your neck, making your chin parallel with the ground.

Circling In the same position as in the previous exercise, circle each ankle in turn, clockwise then anti-clockwise. This helps to relax the legs and increase circulation. Do the same with your wrists. Circle your shoulders backwards.

Arm lifting In the same starting position, lift your arms above your head and then slowly out to each side until parallel to the floor. Now bring each arm back to clasp your hands behind the chair at seat level, feeling the shoulders work. Lastly lift the left arm up and slowly bend from waist to the right to feel a stretch in the left waistline. Repeat to the other side.

amount of pressure the hard worker is under. If you feel that is your situation, the very first thing you should do is talk about it.

Your dependants may be willing to make changes for the sake of your health. Discuss whether, for example, you can manage on less money. Can another member of the household provide a source of additional income? Is there a complete life change you could try as a family, involving different work altogether? Could your partner support you while you retrain for a job you would find more enjoyable and therefore less taxing? And so on.

Talking to your employer, if you have one, may also help. Discuss whether, for example, they realize how much work you have to get through and that it is putting you under intolerable pressure. Can some of your workload be reallocated? Try suggesting ways in which your workload could be decreased (a new computer, for instance). Would job-sharing or part-time work be an option?

Could you be moved sideways? If an employer values you, he or she may well be willing to make changes.

If not, the answer may simply be to begin applying for new jobs in your chosen sphere until you find one where the long-term prognosis for overwork seems remote. Once in a new job, start as you mean to go on and don't be bullied or persuaded into the old pattern of overwork. It's easier to prevent this situation than it is to get out of it.

You may also want to look at your own personality and emotions – perhaps you are motivated by a desire to please; perhaps you are a perfectionist who spends unnecessarily long hours on tasks; perhaps you actually use long work hours as an excuse not to deal with problems in your home relationship or the loneliness of living alone.

Many people live to work because that is all they see. You are, however, important for your own self. For a balanced and energized life you need to investigate life outside work, and your own worth. It is also important to examine whether the work you're currently doing is actually right for you. Step 4 will help you to look more closely at all these areas.

Short-term stress

For most people, stress levels rise and fall many times during a typical day. They fall when we are doing something familiar and mildly pleasing, or when we are with familiar people or by ourselves and under no particular pressure. They rise when we have to face certain situations, social interactions or events. Here we look at 'situation stress' and how to cope with it.

Most of the signs of situation stress are classic signs of anxiety or even fear, both of which can be mentally paralysing and therefore de-energizing. Others are signs of anger, nerves or frustration, which create an adrenalin rush that can, from time to time, be energizing, but can leave you drained and exhausted. These are the emotions that happen when we are faced with a situation in which we don't want to be.

Signs of situation stress

- Your heart begins to race.
- You sweat.
- Your mouth goes dry.
- You tremble.
- You feel nauseous.
- You feel like 'letting off steam' by shouting, swearing, running away.
- Conversely, you feel paralysed and unable to function.
- You feel faint, dizzy, weak.

In fact, not all situation stress is bad. We all occasionally need to face things that we would rather not face – this is what used to be called 'character building' and it helps us to discover our limits. If we never step out of line or try things about which we are unsure, life will become stagnant, boring and enervating. It's the frisson of excitement that creates energy, and that is what Step 4 is all about. If you like, good fear is the opposite of boredom.

However, if you lead the kind of life where situation stress happens very frequently throughout the day – day in, day out – then you will be drained of energy and operating well below par.

Here are some typical examples of situation stress:

- You are running late for work because of a transport strike. Worse – you are running late and you will miss the start of the most important meeting of the year.
- Your lunch date hasn't shown up. You dropped everything to get here – and where did it get you?
- You have to make your first speech to an audience of 500 in just under 15 minutes.
- Your nanny has just rung to say she's unwell and won't be able to make it today.
- You get home late, go to run a bath and the water's cold.

You can probably think of hundreds more. Modern life is full of stress situations, simply because we do so much more than we used to. So the more YOU do, the more likely it is that your day will contain stress. Each little stress episode may not be much, but they add up to a lot.

If you analyse the stress examples above, you'll see that they are almost all events that were 'out of your hands'. This takes us back to the 'inevitability' syndrome that we discussed on page 115. If something happens that is beyond your control, then you should adopt a two-step recovery technique: 1, accept; 2, compensate.

To accept a situation, always practise your breathing techniques, as taught in Step 1. If you can relax, your body you will also relax your mind. Don't take what has happened personally; it can and does happen to everyone. Lastly, think about next week and say to yourself, 'Next week, will this [whatever the situation is] matter?' The answer will almost always be, 'No.'

To compensate for a situation, ask yourself what you can do. If there is something you can do, do it (e.g. if late for work, ring through on your mobile and forewarn). If there isn't, make the best of the new situation (e.g. if late for work and stuck in traffic or on a train without a mobile phone, read or do some paperwork).

These two measures will considerably reduce your stress levels and the accompanying symptoms.

Some of the situations can be avoided in future if you have the time or energy to prevent them – which may be preferable. For example, perhaps you could have made sure all the family knew what time you would be home and wanting a bath, and requested that no one else had one immediately beforehand. Or perhaps you could have rung the lunch date before you left for the restaurant, to make sure that they had remembered your meeting. Forethought can prevent much stress, but beware of trying too hard – you can't possibly second-guess every single situation.

Then there are the stress situations which aren't 'out of your hands' but of your own making. One example from the list above is the speech that you have to make. You must have agreed to make the speech, therefore you really do have to feel the fear and do it anyway. If you hate it and never want to make another speech, next time, say no.

Many people who suffer frequent stress situations of their own making do so because they don't like feeling that they can't carry something off, so they keep trying until they get it right. This is a good attitude, and a large percentage of the time it will work. There comes a point, however, when you have to be realistic. If you are racked with nerves and make a fool of yourself every single time you have to stand up in front of an audience – even though you've done it dozens of times – leave it to someone else. You can't be wonderful at everything!

Other people simply hate to say no. In which case, saying no to someone is a mini stress situation in itself, but will save you a lot of heartache, worry, anxiety, panic, fear and so on in the long run. Learn to say no and save yourself lots of stress. However, if there is no getting out of something you have to do, remember that lots of preparation, lots of sleep and rest beforehand – and a small shot of whisky, perhaps – can make things go much, much better.

Lastly, if your days are filled with stress situations running into each other with little respite, you need to consider your lifestyle and how you can alter it. Exactly the same as long-term overwork, long-term stresses, however varied, can and will deplete your energy and affect your health. You need regular periods of low-stress, relaxation and 'self time' in order for your body to recover. Make sure you get them.

Long-term stress

It is strange how, just when there is nothing to worry about, you worry anyway. Many people live their lives with an almost-constant underlying feeling of slight fear or anxiety – as if something is about to happen and you can't prevent it, because you're not at all sure what it is. Other people live with these constant negative emotions and DO know what their fears are. Will I make enough money to live on for the rest of my life? What will I do if my partner dies? What if something happens to one of the children? What if I get cancer?

Long-term negative thoughts and feelings are very enervating. The fear of what MIGHT happen in life often stops people from enjoying life at all. This manifests itself in depression, low energy levels, fatigue, unease and perhaps psychosomatic illnesses, such as digestive disorders, eczema, unexplained aches and pains.

One cause of such feelings is often simply boredom – a life not rich or fulfilling enough, with too much time for these negatives to enter your psyche and grow. This is a vicious circle, as you can see, because then the negatives cramp you even further and the lethargy is likely to get worse. There is no point telling someone caught in this downward spiral to 'pull themselves together', because they are often incapable of it.

Sufferers of this type of stress – which is a form of mild, moderate or, sometimes, severe depression – may need professional help to aid them in reversing the direction of the spiral. A course of anti-depressants from their GP and/or a course of counselling will almost certainly help.

A good counsellor will encourage you to face your fears and to ask yourself whether or not they are real. If the answer is 'no' or only 'perhaps', then you will be counselled on how to deal with your imagined fears. If the answer is 'yes, they are real', you will be encouraged to see whether you can do anything about them. If the answer is 'yes' again, you will be encouraged to action. And if the answer is 'no', you will be encouraged to accept your life as it is and live day to day. If you can be encouraged to think about tomorrow in terms of 'Now what would I like tomorrow to be?', and gradually find ways to MAKE tomorrow (or even the rest of today) what you want, then the negatives should find it harder to get a hold. This is the principle of 'brief therapy', and many people have been helped to new energy and hope with brief therapy counselling. If you would like to know more, see the Appendix.

Otherwise, helping yourself to a more positive attitude may work. The key questions to ask are:

- Are my fears real?
- If so, what can I do to deal with them?
- If not, what positive thoughts/actions can I use to replace them with?
- What do I want to do with the rest of today?

You should also read the next section, In Pursuit of Happiness. Many people miss the truly valuable things in life that are all around them because they are too busy looking further afield, or worrying that they might lose what they have.

In pursuit of happiness

Prince Charles once famously remarked, 'Love – whatever that is ...' He was right, although he got castigated at the time. Happiness is similarly intangible, with a different meaning for each of us, and yet it is worth seeking, because if you are 'happy', you are energized. You cannot have total energy without feeling that your life is good.

Just as you can manage negative emotions and learn to reduce stress, so you can encourage positive emotions too. This section will show how you can enhance your energy levels through cultivating the state of happiness. It isn't as elusive as it might seem.

What is 'happiness'?

Short-term happiness may be described as pleasure – 'quick fixes' that make you feel good for a while. Long-term happiness is a more general state, perhaps best defined as feeling that your life is worthwhile and that you like – or even love – life. This feeling can take many different forms: it can include peace, contentment, anticipation, excitement, or even simply the absence of negatives. Try the quiz here to see how happy you are:

Happiness quotient quiz

Tick a column for each of the 8 questions and add up your score

	Rarely/never	Sometimes	Often
1 I wake up in the morning looking forward to the day ahead.	0	3	5
2 I enjoy my own company.	0	3	5
3 Others seek me out.	0	3	5
4 It doesn't take much to please me.	0	3	5
5 I enjoy the company of others.	0	3	5
6 My days are full and varied.	0	3	5
7 Generally, I feel fulfilled and content.	0	3	5
8 I seek goals and go for them.	0	3	5

Your score

15 or under: You have a low happiness quotient at the moment. You can alter that by taking on board the advice on these pages and then reading Step 4.

16–29: You would probably describe yourself as moderately happy, but feel that you are missing out on the bigger picture. Be less passive about finding happiness – get up and find the missing elements.

30 or over: Your happiness quotient is high – you appreciate the true value of things, situations and people, and know how to make the most of your life. Your energy levels are also likely to be high.

What happiness isn't

Ask people what would make them really happy and many will reply 'winning the lottery'; in other words, material wealth and the objects associated with it – the mansion, the fast car, the fabulous holidays, the champagne and caviare – are what a majority of people equate with happiness.

Yet, ironically, research shows that a much higher proportion of wealthy people (particularly those who have come by their wealth suddenly) are unhappy than less well-off people. All the trappings that come with wealth will keep most people happy for only a short time. That is because it is not what you have that makes you happy, but how you think about what you do have, and how you react to it.

Consider children at Christmas, when they receive a toy which they have craved for months. Chances are, two days after Christmas it will lie abandoned somewhere and they will be playing with something old and worthless.

Material goods are not happiness and, therefore, however poor you are, you can be happy.

How you can choose happiness

Your happiness doesn't lie in some mythical state in the future... it is now. You can practise being happy – by thinking and reacting to what happens TODAY in a positive and cheerful way. Plan for good things that you can help to happen tomorrow. If you don't know what they might be – keep a Mood Diary (see overleaf) for a week. Don't be passive about happiness; don't sit and wait for it to arrive. Engineer it!

Very importantly, learn to spot happiness in yourself, happy times, happy moods, external things that cheer you. Most of us take life for granted and forget to look out for these positive things.

If you don't believe me, look back over your life now. Think of a time when you felt particularly happy or content. Now you can see that you WERE happy – but at the time, I bet you didn't think about it or realize it. You simply existed and took the situation for granted. What a shame. Practise seeing the happiness NOW. Try these tips:

DO

- Count your blessings on a regular basis.
- Compare yourself to people you know who are worse off than you, not better off.
- Nurture friends and family.
- Appreciate your surroundings.
- Look out for small moments of joy – a sighting of a rare wild flower or a first picking of perfect strawberries.
- Accept that most happiness doesn't come along with fireworks, trumpets and a town crier, but in quiet ways – keep your mind open to your own happiness.

• Accept that life isn't open-ended – you have only a certain time here. DON'T

• Indulge in self-pity. It is easy to get into a negative spiral when, with self-help, you can get on a positive one.

• Blame other people for your lack of happiness. Others are not responsible. It is up to you to make choices to improve your happiness quotient.

• Blame a bad situation for your lack of happiness. Why is it, for instance, that some people with a physical disability are extremely cheerful and enjoy life, while others get depressed and feel their life has ended? Remember, it is how you react and think that is most important WHATEVER the situation.

Obviously you cannot expect to feel happy 100 per cent of your life. Tragic and horrible things may happen to you; annoying, upsetting and sad things probably will happen to you. To live life to the full, in any case, you have to experience a wide range of emotions – don't be afraid of sadness, for example. However, if you have a deep-down core of self-love and life-love, and the positive attitude that makes you happy when all other things are equal, you will cope with the truly bad times with more energy – in other words, you will deal with them better.

In Step 4, we will be examining all the ways in which you can increase your enjoyment of life – the 'worthwhile' factor. Step 4 will help you to be happy, both short-term and long-term.

For further information and help in managing your emotions, with courses, therapies, etc., see the Appendix.

Keeping a mood diary

For seven days, at the end of each day, record your moods throughout the day and what you were doing at the time.

FOR EXAMPLE:

11 a.m, Sunday

Bored Reading the Sunday papers as usual

1 p.m.

Pleased Rose rang, haven't heard from her in ages

At the end of the week you will have built up a picture of what makes you happy. In the example above, it is already obvious that perhaps a life too full of predictable routine may make this person bored, whereas if they make more effort to keep in touch with friends, they are more likely to feel happy.

In general, cut down on non-happiness-producing situations and increase the activities that make you feel good.

Step 3 round-up

AT THE END OF STEP 3, YOU SHOULD BE FEELING MUCH MORE THAT YOU CAN CONTROL YOUR LIFE.

• You should have a greater understanding of your 'self' – the negatives, the pluses, the failings, the strengths, the de-energizers in your personality and the ways you can improve and thus increase your energy. You should be working on those ideas every day.

• You should have a greater understanding of your role in the world, how to change it if you need to, and how to react in an energizing and positive way towards others. This is all about conserving or creating energy, not wasting it.

• Step 4 will take you further – examining how you can HARNESS your energy and achieve the pinnacle, the absolute top of the energy spiral, when the force of your own energy creates even more for itself. Prepare to push back your boundaries and see just what you can achieve.

Now say:

I can go as far as I want in the direction I choose

....and move on to Step 4

step 4

Pushing Back your Boundaries

Open your mind and relearn the keys to self-expression and fulfilment

You have learnt how to energize your body through relaxation, exercise and diet, and you have released yourself from energy-draining situations and attitudes. In other words, as you begin Step 4 you are running at maximum energy-efficiency. The 'building' that we discussed earlier is complete and strong.

Now that you do have lots of energy to spare, Step 4 is all about harnessing this energy to create even more. Think of it as all the 'optional extras' that make your building so much more pleasant and enjoyable – the accessories, the decor, the plants in the garden. Also think of Step 4 as helping you to feel confident and free enough to lock the door behind you and leave home – to go out and explore the world beyond.

The fact is that what pleases you will energize you. What stimulates you in a positive way will energize you. What motivates you will energize you. Why did you want energy in the first place, if not to use it to enhance your life?

In Step 4 we help you to discover all the ways and directions in which you can channel your new-found energy to broaden or deepen your life. Just see how far you can go.

We take a long look at short-term pleasures and motivators and long-term motivation, the meaning of ambition and the importance of purpose. We then look at fear versus security, and excitement versus contentment.

Ultimately, you will actually discover that energy isn't finite – you don't need to feel that you have just 'so much' energy that will allow you to do just 'this many' things and no more. Once you finally tap into life as you truly want to live it, you will find that energy really is infinite.

And infinite energy is total energy.

Week 4

General notes

Don't forget to continue with your ongoing regular:

- stretching,
- yoga,
- massage
- diet ,
- exercise,

plans this week.

Remember to continue working on the weaker areas of your energy as described in Step 3.

Day 1

- Read through Step 4.
- Do the Balancing Act questionnaire (overleaf), check your results and see exactly how good you are at leading a balanced and fulfilled life.

Day 2

- Use pages 150–51 to work out how well you manage to make time for yourself.
- Write down a checklist of some ideas for giving yourself more time on a regular basis.

Day 3

- Check through the ideas given in the section on short-term energizers (see pages 152–5).
- How many of the ideas there do you manage to take on board each day?

Day 4

- How much time do you devote to thinking? Think about it – see pages 155–6.

Day 5

- Move on to reading and absorbing the section on long-term energizers (pages 158–62).
- How ambitious are you? Do you have some long-term goals? Write them down.

Day 6

- Read the section on how to get what you want (see pages 163–4) and make a checklist of your own goals.
- Work out how you can improve your own chances of achieving more.
- Check the list of ideal traits (see page 164) and see how you rate.

Day 7

- Appraise how you have done during the 28 days of the programme.
- Do you feel more positive?
- Do you find your mental and physical energy increasing?
- Continue working with the programme to produce your goal – total energy.

TURN THE PAGE TO START STEP FOUR

The balancing act

How good are you at balancing your life and making time for yourself? Are you a well-rounded person and fulfilled as an individual? Or are there great gaps in your life and large imbalances in your behaviour which are also unbalancing your energy?

The questionnaire that follows is designed to help you find out how fulfilling your life currently is. You need to answer all the questions totally honestly. Then add up your scores for each section and read my analysis of your current strengths and weaknesses, before progressing to the next sections.

Tick one box on each line

A = rarely / never B = sometimes C = a lot / all the time

Section 1

STATEMENT	A	B	C
I work longer than average hours.	○	○	○
I put work before social arrangements.	○	○	○
I do chores around the home (e.g. cleaning, washing).	○	○	○
I agree to do things for friends/ family that I don't really want to do.	○	○	○
I exercise to keep myself healthy.	○	○	○
I read books/papers/etc for education rather than pleasure.	○	○	○
I tell the truth even if it puts me in a bad light.	○	○	○
I feel I have an obligation to fulfil my parents' expectations of me.	○	○	○
I give money/time to charity.	○	○	○
I consider other people's needs /preferences before my own.	○	○	○
Add up the ticks in each column			

Section 2

STATEMENT	A	B	C
I enjoy my home life and find contentment there.	○	○	○
I enjoy my own company.	○	○	○
I can think of plenty to do if I have no TV available.	○	○	○
I get a lot of birthday and Christmas cards.	○	○	○
I do things on the spur of the moment.	○	○	○
I find plenty to laugh about.	○	○	○
I initiate social events.	○	○	○
I find it pleasurable to learn.	○	○	○
I surprise myself by what I can enjoy.	○	○	○
I travel to new places.	○	○	○
Add up the ticks in each column			

Section 3

STATEMENT	A	B	C
I think about the future.	○	○	○
I enjoy making plans.	○	○	○
I meet new people.	○	○	○
I look out for new ideas.	○	○	○
I feel frightened or excited.	○	○	○
I decide to do something that will create great upheaval.	○	○	○
I take a risk.	○	○	○
I have a clear picture of how I'd like to be in ten years' time.	○	○	○
I accept a long-term challenge.	○	○	○
I feel that life's too short for all I want to do.	○	○	○
Add up the ticks in each column			

Now transfer your scores to the spaces at the top of the next page and find the relevant information below.

Section 1			Section 2			Section 3		
A	B	C	A	B	C	A	B	C

Section 1

Mostly As You seem to have an underdeveloped sense of duty and/or responsibility and probably a very low boredom threshold. You may be thought selfish. If coupled with mostly Cs in Section 2, you're primarily a pleasure-seeker. Sometimes you are high on energy, but then you'll collapse with exhaustion. You usually enjoy life but, as you get older, you may find it starts feeling empty – if you haven't already, secretly, had that feeling. Pace yourself more and realize happiness and energy aren't just NOW things. Try to replace immediate gratification with long-term and solid things. Pages 158–64 will help.

Mostly Bs You have an average-to-good sense of morality and are usually fairly quick to pick up on other people's feelings and to fulfil obligations. It is likely that you have a good balance between your work and your social life but, if you scored high on As in Sections 2 or 3, take care to find opportunities to expand your life and make time for yourself.

Mostly Cs You have an overdeveloped sense of duty and a strong need to please others. You may also feel depressed, with a feeling that you are missing out on the lighter side of life but are unsure how to alter that. You are usually unable to feel good being selfish and/or spending a lot of time on yourself. Your owe it, in fact, not only to yourself but to others, to find out who you really are underneath your sensible, dogged mantle. Use the rest of this Step to help you get the confidence and the ideas for expanding your life and increasing time and opportunities for self-expression.

Section 2

Mostly As You are not truly in touch with your feelings or with your potential to live and enjoy each day. If coupled with a high score of Cs in Section 1, you are probably a workaholic, leading a very unbalanced life and lacking in energy. If coupled with a high score of Cs in Section 3, you tend to live too much in the future and forget to enjoy the NOW. You are likely to be a 'worrier', with an almost permanent sense of mild anxiety, often taking life too seriously. Use pages 152–7 in this Step to help you appreciate short-term pleasures and release yourself from fear.

Mostly Bs You find it easy to appreciate the finer and smaller things of life and may be content without having huge expectations of life. You are probably a very popular person and possibly the 'life and soul of the party' when you feel in the right mood. You have huge potential, however, which you may not be exploring. Pages 160–64 may give you the incentive to expand your horizons a little.

Mostly Cs You enjoy life to the full on a day-by-day basis. Your energy levels are often high and you tend to live on short but sweet adrenalin rushes, and probably sleep well. Long-term, though, you may run out of energy unless you get more balance into your life. You need more periods of quiet reflection. If coupled with a high score of As in Section 3, you'll benefit from reading pages 158–64 and getting more long-term, less frenetic contentment.

Section 3

Mostly As You tend to live for today – or even yesterday – and you dislike change. Ask yourself why you are a bit afraid of life, because it is certain that you prefer life to be secure, routine and comfortable rather than challenging or full of innovation. If you had a high tally of C scores in Section 1, you are probably hiding behind work and duty in order to avoid stretching yourself. With the new-found energy that you have gained from the first three Steps, and with help from the rest of this Step, don't be a tortoise, be an eagle. See how far you can fly – see just what you can do. You will surprise yourself.

Mostly Bs You seem to have a balanced view of life and what you want from it, as well as what you can give. You rarely suffer from boredom and, if you do, tend to try to do something about it. Use the rest of this Step for more ideas to increase your repertoire!

Mostly Cs You are fearless and energetic, with a strong sense of your own life, past, present and future. You are likely always to be striving for impossible new heights and may find it hard to relax. You feel strongly that you have only one crack at life and don't want to waste a minute. You may, up to a point, be a control freak. Step 1 will have helped you to relax and unwind . Now it is time to find ways of getting simpler, less demanding pleasures and contentment from life. The rest of this Step will help you to achieve that.

All three sections

Mostly As You are likely to be suffering from depression and life may at times seem meaningless and empty to you. You need help in bringing new people, ideas and hope into your life. This book is a good starting point, but don't be afraid to seek professional help too.

Mostly Bs You are highly likely to be a very balanced person, with good natural energy levels and an optimistic, realistic view of life. Maybe you worry that you aren't positive enough in some aspects, though, and the rest of Step 4 may help you to improve that side of your character.

Mostly Cs You need to learn to pace yourself better, otherwise you may 'burn out' before too long, despite what you've learnt in this book. You feel life is to be lived fast, furious and without compromise. Energy, though – as you've found out already – needs to be managed if it is to be finite. Pushing back boundaries can also mean finding quieter and deeper ways to live life.

4 Many people automatically feel guilty if they put themselves first, even now and then. Yet for total energy, everyone needs SELF time – not just once in a while, but every single day. Here's how to do it.

making time for yourself

it isn't selfish to book time for yourself – it's energy-enhancing sense

You can't push back the boundaries and achieve the life you want without making time for yourself in which to think, to plan and do it. Yet many people feel guilty for spending time on themselves. Women are probably the worst at devoting time to themselves without a rush of guilt. There always seems to be something more deserving.

In truth, though, whatever your commitments are, however needy the rest of the family, the work, the house, the garden – if you haven't made enough time for your own needs, long-term all the other things will suffer too. So it isn't selfish to book time for YOU; it is good sense.

In Step 3 we looked at time management and how you can streamline your life to create more time than you thought you had. Now you need to motivate yourself to use that time.

Where do you stand in the scheme of your life?

Look at the following list of things you may typically have on your 'to do' list one evening. Put them in order of how important you think it is that each is done by the end of the evening.

A Sit with sick child and play draughts or similar for half an hour.
B Cook the family a meal.
C Ring best friend for a chat.
D Clean the kitchen floor.
E Pick son up from football match.
F Do pile of ironing.
G Soak in bath and think about plot for new best-selling novel.

Did your order of importance come out like this: A, E, C, G, B, D, F? I doubt if it did – and yet that is the most sensible use of your time. Why?

Well, A is essential; E also is essential (assuming there is no one else available to pick him up); B, D and F are all non-essential but, if you do do them, that is their order of importance. (Yes, the family need to eat, but instead of cooking why not think about a takeaway or getting someone else to cook sometimes?)

Given that B, D and F are not essential, you now move the two things on the list that are purely for you – C and G – up to take their place. YOU time is more important than non-YOU non-essentials. Do the most energetic of the YOU things first – in this instance, phoning your friend – and save the most relaxing until last.

The rule is – if you're not sure how to use your time, FIRST do essential non-YOU items, SECOND do YOU items, and THIRD, if there is any time, do non-essential, non-YOU items. If you're not sure whether something is an essential or a non-essential non-YOU item, ask yourself if it can wait until another day, or be avoided altogether. If the answer is 'yes' to either, it is non-essential. Right? Right.

How much time for you?

You may remember early in the book I asked you to set aside time for relaxation, which can be included in your YOU time. Here is the minimum length your YOU time should be:

Daily Minimum 1 hour. Can be divided up into different YOU pleasures as you wish. Use all the suggestions that follow to give you ideas. Remember, the best time is when essentials are done.

Weekly In addition to your daily YOU time, have a longer weekly YOU session of at least 3 hours. This is vital, as an hour goes quickly and isn't enough to get a good concentrated go at anything creative.

Monthly Have a whole YOU day once a month at least – a fortnight is even better. Do nothing all day except things you really want to do (even if this means relaxing and doing nothing all day). Non-YOU essentials or inessentials shouldn't get a look-in on this day.

Annually Have 2 weeks' YOU time (en bloc or as two separate weeks) when you take a holiday, or do whatever it is that you really want to do. You think this sounds a lot? Add it up. All I am suggesting is that you spend around 47 days in total (including all the individual hours, etc.) devoted to yourself each year. That comes to a mere 13 per cent of your life! Should you feel guilty about that? I think not.

4

You can't have complete energy unless you enjoy your life, because what pleases you will provide energy-enhancing stimulation. Here we look at small and simple ways to get your daily charge of enjoyment.

short-term energizers

plan to do something that pleases you every day – starting now

As we saw at the end of Step 3, pleasure is either instant, immediate and short-term, or slower and longer lasting. On pages 158–64 we will be looking at the longer-term energizers. Here we look at the short-term.

What pleases you will stimulate you. And what stimulates you will energize you. Therefore, it is vital to enjoy life! The good news is that it is no longer necessary to feel guilty about your pleasures – they are doing you good. All research shows that almost everything that forms the lighter side of life and helps you to feel happy actually does help you to be healthier and live longer, mostly by stimulating your immune system and helping in disease prevention. Laughter, music, dancing, being with friends, practical jokes, lovemaking, nice surprises, stroking a pet, getting a special letter – all of these, individually, can seriously improve your health. Imagine the cumulative effect! We also look at short-term motivation – how to channel your energy through thought into purpose and action.

What do you want to do today?

It is an obvious but often forgotten fact that all you really have is now, this second. It follows that if you use each spare second in a way that pleases you, the seconds will add up to a life that pleases you. So harness your energy to make full use of the present. Of course you need to think of the future sometimes, but the knock-on effect of enjoying NOW is vital to your energy levels.

Below are some areas of short-term pleasure that many adults forget. See what you can incorporate into your daily life (not just in your YOU time, but all day long), choosing the ideas that most please you, and then see how much more lively and vital you feel.

Remember to laugh

As we get older, it is easy to take life too seriously. It's also easy to think that laughter is for the young and that the silly side of life is somehow undignified. As all research shows laughter has numerous beneficial effects on your health and well-being as well as your longevity, perhaps THAT idea is the silly one. Laughter raises the levels of 'good' hormones in your body and lowers blood pressure.

It is easy to get into the habit of 'sense of humour failure' and out of the habit of nurturing your crazy side. Remember, laughter doesn't have to be of the slapstick variety – it is what turns YOU on that is funny. If you feel that you haven't had much laughter in your life lately, think back to what did used to make you laugh... who you thought was funny... which friends made you laugh... which friends brought out your own ability to make them laugh. You need actively to seek out 'laughter opportunities'. It's all too easy to wallow in sadness. If there is a choice of a good comedy or a serious programme on TV, watch the comedy (record the other if you like). Read books with some humour in them – there are humourous novels to suit all levels of intellect.

Remember to use your body

Any activity that uses your body will increase your well-being and the flow of energy. It can be anything – sex, dancing, cycling, whatever you like. If you can't think of anything else to do NOW – get moving. (If you can't remember all the benefits of activity, turn back to page 81.)

Remember to pamper your body

At least once a day you should give yourself over to some utterly hedonistic physical pampering. This can be anything that you find gorgeous – a long neck-and-shoulder massage, a soothing aromatherapy bath, a manicure, a visit to the hairdresser's, a session of sex with your partner where he or she does all the giving and you just lie there and take, a few best-quality chocolates eaten slowly and without guilt...

Alleviate boredom

Anyone's life will have its share of routine tasks. If life were exciting 100 per cent of the time, then excitement would become the new boredom. The trick is simply to minimize the amount of boring routine and, having done that, to accept what is left, while finding your own ways of alleviating the boredom of the routine, perhaps even elevating it on to a new level. Even doing an old chore in a new way can bring pleasure. Otherwise, if it is something you can do without thought, use any routine time for extra Think Time (see opposite). While your body is on autopilot your brain is free to go where it wants.

Books – including audio books – and music can be used to add enjoyment to routine tasks or dull journeys, so never go anywhere without both book and personal audiogear. Should you have times when you are simply sitting there feeling bored because you can't think of anything to do, read on.

Element of surprise

If your day is mapped out clearly, it is time-efficient but it can be dreary. Bring an element of unpredictability into your life and engineer yourself some surprises. Enter competitions, ring a radio station, try a new set of shops, go to work by a different route or method. Get a street map of your town, find somewhere you've never been before and go there. Buy yourself a bouquet of flowers. Also think of surprises for other people – pleasant ones, of course. That can bring you just as much enjoyment as being on the receiving end – and the recipient may return the compliment at a later date.

Be a child

Young children look at the world around them in wonder and seem to notice everything. As we get older, we take it all for granted. Cultivate the child in yourself – instead of hurrying through your day with blinkers on, stop for a few seconds to appreciate small things, familiar objects and simple pleasures.

Look – Watch the flames of a fire; inspect the blossom on a cherry tree close up; take in the colours and forms of trees, buildings, hills – wherever you live there will be things of beauty or strength to inspire you. Seek out the images that please you. When away from home, take photos of loved ones and of images that please you, and look at them frequently.

Listen – Make a point of listening to the early morning birdsong; insects in the garden or park; small children laughing in the playground; music. This all might sound corny but it's a valid part of life.

Touch – Feel velvet, satin and silk and appreciate its texture; stroke a rose petal or a cat.

Smell – Drink in the aroma of new-mown grass, newly baked bread, a meal cooking, a flower, a herb garden, a slice of ripe melon.

Contact – Make the most of every opportunity, however small, for close contact with people you like – hug, kiss, talk, listen, touch. People who are hugged regularly thrive!

Taste – Don't eat or drink with your mind shut – taste it all, develop your sense of different flavours.

Be with friends

Try to have some contact with at least one friend every day – just a quick catch-up phone call or a 10-minute visit will do if you have no more time. Friends stimulate and energize you – at least they should.

Most of us have one or two friends who seem to achieve the reverse, making us feel depressed and drained when we talk to them. Be quite firm about how much time and effort you expend on such people if they are that way all the time. Of course all friends get down from time to time and it is your 'duty' to cheer them up and help them resolve their problems, which in itself can be stimulating, but this should really be an occasional thing (and something they will do for you as necessary in return), not an on-going state of affairs.

Relax

Don't forget to have a relax session every day, taking whatever form of relaxation pleases you at the time. This could be just lying on your bed with your eyes shut or in a scented bath with candles and book; reading and listening to music; doing some gentle stretches in a candlelit room; meditation.

Think Time

The second energizing element of your day involves making time to think. How often do you travel inside your head? What do you want? What do you feel?

You can't find the answers to what will make you tick – function well – unless you ask the questions. This needs Think Time. Build it into your day. Certainly use part – or all, sometimes – of your YOU time to think.

You can use all kinds of situations to extend your think time – in the bath, while travelling (not if you're driving, of course), while doing mundane or routine chores.

Such thinking, if you're not used to it, can be hard at first. There are various types of productive thinking, each of which has its own use. Try to do some of each regularly for balanced and energizing Think Time:

Daydreaming – Start off thinking about something or someone pleasant and let your mind wander or free-fall from there. Where do you go? Sometimes, when you're free-falling, your mind will keep going back to a certain point (it could be a worry or an unsolved dilemma) and you need to use your Think Time to sort it out, otherwise it will keep recurring and stopping you from thinking of other things. Let daydreaming take you where it wants to go, and at the end always ask yourself, 'Is there any of that that I can really do?' Almost all the best ideas and life-enhancing changes come from daydreaming sessions.

Planning – This type of Think Time needs a method of note-taking, be it pen and paper, lap-top or dictaphone. You have a project in mind and you want to work out how to take it further. Write or say everything as it occurs to you, then sort it out logically later.

Self-searching – Thinking about you, your motives, your faults and so on, and use what has happened to improve what will happen in the future. In other words, be your own psychoanalyst. Ask yourself, 'Why did I do that?' 'Why did I react that way?' 'Could I have done it better?' End the session with making at least one decision and one resolution. For example, 'I over-reacted when my wife said she'd had coffee with an old boyfriend she bumped into. I am going to apologize and try to be less jealous.'

Without regular Think Time, you won't be in control of your life, short- or long-term. Get in the habit of thinking about all the input that forms your daily life. Much of what your brain processes may be rubbish, but if even 10 per cent is life-altering it's well worth doing.

Purpose in your day

A sense of purpose to the day is as important to your pleasure as all the transitory senses. For true energy, you need to cultivate the habit of waking each day, knowing what it is you want to achieve.

If you scored mainly As in our questionnaire on pages146-7 (especially Section 3), your days probably lack form and purpose. There are, though, many ways to inject a sense of form into your life. Use your Think Time to work out what it is that you want, what it is that you can give. Long-term ideas and projects are covered in more detail in the following section. If you need extra help, use some of these ideas:

• Check out the local library. Your library is a haven of ideas and information, and yet only one in 100 of the population uses a library regularly! The non-fiction sections are perfect for browsing through to find ideas for projects, hobbies, education and so on.

If you have a computer, the Internet is a vast library in your own home, but be warned – you need to be strong about how you use it, as many people have found themselves wasting vast amounts of time and energy on the Net for little or no return in terms of life enhancement. It should be treated like a good wine – a little, now and then, to be savoured.

• Check out the news. Newspapers, both local and national, free advertising magazines, local websites for local information – keeping abreast of local, national and international news is a great way of inputting ideas. Sooner or later something will spark off an idea or connection and you will be fired with enthusiasm.

• Think of an area of your life that you have been neglecting and see what you can do to embrace it. For example, you have been eating badly. Check up on healthy eating and make a list of resolutions to improve.

• Think of someone else that you know and think of something you can do to improve their life. For example, your elderly neighbour has trouble maintaining her garden. Can you help? Or can you find out for her what help is available locally? Once you think of an idea don't abandon it, see it through.

Every day is a new adventure if you want it to be. The more you explore the possibilities, the more you will see how it really is the case that energy creates energy.

The next section is concerned with long-term life energizers, but don't forget that a long-term project can be worked on in small amounts every day. We all need some projects like this in our lives.

4

The basis of emotional energy is having a feeling of real purpose, plus a sense of anticipation. Without these, life can easily become dull and meaningless, leading to an enveloping sense of lethargy.

long-term energizers

long-term motivation is the key to ongoing high energy levels in your life

While superficial pleasures and a daily feeling of contentment are important to help boost your energy levels, it is the long-term that matters even more. In this section we look at how you can explore the possibilities of life and your own potential to maximize them. This is the final goal in your search for total energy.

Why are you here?

This is not an impertinent question, but an important one. Why do you think you are alive? What are you doing with your life? You get through the days, maybe feel content enough, and yet do you feel as if you are really in the driving seat – living life as you really want to live it? Even if you are in the driving seat, that's not much use unless you're heading along the right road. Are YOU?

You may not mind whether or not you leave a mark on the world – we can't all be an Einstein or a Bill Gates – but you surely mind whether or not you end your life with a sense of achievement, in that you have achieved a life that YOU feel has been worthwhile. This is being at ease with yourself and without guilt.

You may say, 'I'm quite happy with my life as it is. I am content. I don't need grand plans and ideas.' Good. That may be fine. Indeed, getting through life in one piece, making a reasonable job of it, is worthwhile in itself and more than many of us manage. Sometimes, however, contentment may be no more than an absence of misery – in which case why have a negative when you can have a positive? I would also surmise that you wouldn't be reading this book if you felt that you already had enough energy; that 'contentment' may be another way of saying 'boredom' – and that boredom equals lack of energy, just as anticipation and excitement and challenge equal a boost to adrenalin and a boost to energy.

Be very honest with yourself before assuming that you don't need this section.

The importance of purpose

It's not necessary to map out a life-plan for every minute of the time you have left. If you are TOO focused on a certain thing, you won't be tempted to turn off down the uncharted side roads that can also be exciting and therefore energizing. Indeed, many people find that in taking a chance on such a route, they hit upon the One Big Thing for them.

However, a 'rough idea' IS a good idea. Knowing roughly want you want (which also entails knowing yourself), and knowing how to achieve it, give your life purpose and focus, and give you a sense of ambition, which in turn is extremely energizing.

Purpose, focus and ambition are often misunderstood. Many people shy away from all three, feeling that they are for those who are young, professional and aggressive. Yet they are three very important attributes for anyone. They certainly don't just relate to the young, and they don't just relate to your work. They should be a part of every area of your life.

Purpose and ambition will drive you to succeed and motivate you in the strongest way, and focus will help you to achieve what you want. Whether you want to change your job, learn a language, find a partner or run a marathon, those are the unchanging things you need.

Purpose, focus, ambition = energy = fulfilment

– but don't forget the odd sidetrack too!

What do YOU want?

First you need to surf your own mind to decide what your goals may be. In the last section we discussed Think Time which can be used to do this. If you need help, the selection of nine ideas below may be a starting point.

As a general rule, you will help the flow of long-term energy if your goals fit in with the following criteria:

• They are balanced. Goals which balance each other are ideal – for example, a 'learning' goal balances a 'physical achievement' goal. A 'travel' goal balances a 'community' goal. However, the exception proves the rule and if a goal energizes you strongly enough, it could prove to be a life's worth of fulfilment with no balancers – for example, several of the world's greatest scientists and artists sacrificed the rest of their lives to follow a path for life without diversion.

• They are achievable. It is, however, a big drain on your energy to go for the impossible. That isn't to say that you shouldn't try to live out some of your fantasies. There is a difference.

We shall be discussing these topics, and how to get what you want, in more detail later in this section.

Nine fulfilling ideas

1 SELF-KNOWLEDGE A good starting point is always that of learning more about yourself and what makes you tick. This will certainly increase your chances of picking ideal goals and motivators through the rest of your life.

You may choose to do this through personal therapy, if you can afford it, or through seminars and evening classes, or privately through books and other research, as well as introspection (Think Time). It may help to write down your thoughts. Useful addresses and reading matter appear in the Appendix.

Everyone should do this regularly, because we all change and if you don't stop to examine yourself you may not realize just how much you have changed and, therefore, you won't alter your life accordingly.

2 EDUCATION Leaving school or college is just the beginning of your education, not the end. What do you want to know more about? If you have a book, or a teacher, or some other means of learning at your disposal, then you can improve your life. You can develop your intellect, your knowledge, your skills, your understanding. NOTE: Long periods of reading can be enervating – intersperse them with short periods of physical activity, or a change of mental activity.

3 CAREER BOOSTERS Your job is a huge part of your future life and so you should regularly evaluate how it is going – how you feel about what you do, whether there are any changes to be made?

Of all the ideas on this page, this is probably the most important in terms of the effect it can have on your energy levels.

Ask yourself whether or not you enjoy your job. Have you changed so much that you no longer feel comfortable with it? Or has it changed so much? List other possible jobs that you would like to try. However outlandish they seem, put them down.

Investigate retraining possibilities, bank finance, or whatever you need to pursue the career you want. Don't be frightened to 'downshift' – do something less high-profile – if that appeals to you.

Remember that you have more skills than you think you have. For example, if you are brilliant at helping to sort out friends' problems, perhaps you could train to become a counsellor. If you are always complimented on the beauty of your garden, you could go into horticulture, and so on. The Escape Committee can help you retrain (see the Appendix).

4 MONEYMAKING Face it, one of our strongest motivators is the instinct to survive – and nowadays that means having enough money to provide us and our dependants with a reasonable lifestyle. It's why people often stay in jobs that they dislike for years. You may be forgiven for thinking that the more money you can accumulate, the better. As we saw in the earlier section on happiness, though, more money doesn't always mean more happiness.

Interestingly, people's ideas of how much is enough vary enormously. One recent writer in a national newspaper reckoned that anyone could be happy, and live well, on £20,000 a year, which would include running a car, a decent annual holiday plus socializing and so on. He feels that this is the perfect amount and that any more would just confuse the issue. Another feature in another national newspaper article the same week said that to live well for the rest of his life, a lottery winner would need to win at least £5 million! Assuming that the winner is, say, 40 and has another 40 years to live, that works out at £125,000 a year – something of a difference.

I think the truth is that the pursuit of money for its own sake is rarely the route to happiness – and often the cause of much wasted energy. The best kind of money to make is the kind that comes almost as an aside, from doing something you really love and then finding that someone wants to pay you for it!

What is really important, though, is to have enough balance in your life (and enough spare time) to enjoy the fruits of your earnings and, indeed, the parts of your life that no money can buy – family, friends and all the other ideas listed here. If you can't do that, you might as well not bother.

5 RELATIONSHIPS People are ambitious about work and about personal achievement – but rarely about how far they can develop their friendships, family relationships and so on. Take some time to consider whether your output regarding the people you care about matches what you feel for them inside. What can you do to enhance these relationships? If you feel you don't have enough relationships, then see what you can do to improve that situation.

6 CREATIVITY Everyone is creative, it is just a matter of tapping into what you are good at and/or what gives you pleasure. Creativity isn't just being able to paint a picture or write a book. It's about being able to do almost anything with your own personal stamp on it. Any hobby is creative.

If there is something you always wanted to try but lack of confidence is stopping you, start now. For ideas, begin at the hobby section of the library. I have seen several individuals change from lethargic people into dynamos of energy once they found their true creative talent.

7 TRAVEL I know people who have stayed in the same village all their lives and never travelled. I know people who go to the same resort, same guest house, on holiday every year, in the same week. I suppose television brings the world to many people and perhaps that is enough, but there is almost nothing as enriching as travelling. Whether it's a backpack walking holiday or a first-class flight to China, it's educative, exciting, challenging and energizing. Just planning a trip can be a huge energy boost in itself. Don't wait until you've got lots of money – do it now.

8 PHYSICAL ACHIEVEMENT Step 2 showed how physical health and fitness are important for energy. Having found that out, you might like to take it further. See just how far you can push back the boundaries, see what you can actually do with your body. Do you perhaps want to run a marathon? Learn to abseil? Waterski? Walk the length of the land? Take up mountain climbing? Ride a horse? Learn to swim?

9 GOOD WORKS As I mentioned earlier, if you spend too much time feeling put upon by people and being used as a constant shoulder to cry on, it can be enervating. Surprisingly, though, in small doses, doing 'good' can energize you, because it can lift the guilt of selfishness and provide purpose, as well as making you see how lucky you are! Charitable work almost always involves meeting new people, which is a third energizer. Regulate the hours a week that you do devote to it, and don't be put upon to do more than you want to.

In smaller places, members of your local community will be able to suggest openings for you to do an hour or two a week of something 'good'. In cities, ask at the town hall or browse the library or through the Yellow Pages to find ideas that suit your personality. Hospitals, homes for the elderly, drop-in centres and charity shops are always in need of people to help. You may also know a family member or friend who needs help, though beware of offering more commitment than you can give in practice.

Getting what you want

Here are a few pointers to help you improve the odds of achieving whatever it is that you want.

Liking yourself

Think yourself into a positive frame of mind. Tell yourself every day as you look in the mirror that you are the best, and that what you want you can achieve. Tell yourself this before you meet others and before anything you do that is important and challenging. Even if you don't feel confident, act that way and, as research shows, you will actually feel more confident straight away.

Focusing

Whatever you decide to do, give it your all at that time. Focus on the job in hand and don't let your mind stray. Concentrate 100 per cent. Even if you do this for only a short period of time, you will achieve much more. Try to see anything you begin through to its conclusion.

Balancing

Generally, a balanced life promotes good energy flow. Try to get a good balance of needs, aims, goals and other elements in your life. Sometimes you will set everything else aside for the one big challenge, but it is a rare person who can live long-term like this without exhaustion and, of course, if it doesn't work out there isn't much left.

Visualization

Imagine what it is that you want and picture it in your head. For instance, if you have decided that you want to climb Mount Everest, picture yourself there on the top. Who is with you? What do you see? What colours are you wearing? How do you feel? Then go backwards, visualizing all you will need to get to that point – the training, the planning, the commitment.

Realism versus fantasy

When considering the boundaries you want to push back, try to weigh up whether or not you really can achieve that thing. For instance, if you are fit, or can get fit, there is little to stop you climbing Mount Everest. If, however, you've taken early retirement with a heart condition, dreaming of scaling mountain peaks will offer you nothing but frustration.

Make your goals within the bounds of possibility – for every one thing you can't do, there are several, just as fulfilling, that you can.

On the other hand, don't be too quick to limit the possibilities. If you do only what you know you can do, without stretching yourself at all, what's the point? Live out your fantasies as far as you can. Learn to push yourself beyond your normal limits and see how far you can go. You will undoubtedly surprise yourself.

There is nothing wrong with feeling an element of fear or panic – it's another form of adrenalin rush and great in small doses. If you've taken on a big challenge that's keeping you awake at night with fright, break it down into smaller, more manageable parts, so that the fear is bearable. Alternatively, get help! And remember the first rule if you're frightened – action! Just do it. The longer you hang around worrying, the worse it gets. That is true whether you're about to learn to handle a computer at the age of 70 or climb out of the tent and tackle the last stage to that peak.

Going off course

Map out a life plan by all means, but don't limit yourself by determining never to move from the path you're on. At least look in other directions as you stride along, and if you see another path that looks intriguing, take it. You may not see such a path, and that's fair enough, but keep looking. No one's going to shout and scream at you for changing your mind.

If you decide you've made a mistake, don't be afraid to turn around and head back the way that you came. It is much more enervating to stick with mistakes than to just stop, even if you're not sure what will happen.

Intuition

Don't be afraid to rely on your intuition about your life and in all decision-making. Research shows that 80 per cent of the time, following 'hunches' proves the best course of action. Believe in what your heart and brain tell you, and you will stand a much greater chance of success than if you consult someone else!

10 things a life coach will tell you

or, how to make it all happen...

1 Have goals and re-appraise them now and then.
2 Set down your plans for how you're going to achieve them.
3 Visualize yourself achieving them.
4 Remember, other people aren't responsible for your success, you are.
5 Face your fears and deal with them.
6 Be honest with yourself.
7 Don't apologize for living your life.
8 Keep yourself in balance.
9 Enjoy what you do.
10 Remember, energy isn't finite, but your life is.

Energy

isn't finite

but your life is.

make it happen.

start now.

The 3-day programme

This short programme is useful if you have just three days to spare and completely clear. It will help to relax and re-energize you, and give you a taste of what the complete 28-day programme might help you to achieve.

Choose three quiet, free days and read through the programme before you begin.

You will need a few things around you, so make sure that you have the following:

- Your own personal space.
- Essential oils and base oil (see page 26).
- Music and books (including audio books) to help entertain, energize and relax you.
- Detox diet food and drink (see page 54 for what to buy and daily menus).
- Comfortable clothes and shoes.

NOTE Throughout the three days, drink as much as you like of the detox drinks listed on page 53.

the 3-day programme

Day 1

Morning

Get up about 9 a.m.

- Detox breakfast.
- Relaxing bath with essential oils.
- Stretch routine (see pages 36–7).
- Rest and read until lunchtime.
- Detox lunch.

Afternoon

- Walk – as long as you feel like. Pace moderate. Try some deep breathing as you go (page 33).
- Massage – if no partner available, do self-massage as described on pages 29–32.

Evening

- Detox dinner.
- Play music and/or read for as long as you like.
- Practise deep breathing and good posture (see pages 32–5).
- Read the section on sleep (see page 44) and use any tips that might help you.
- Early night.

Day 2

Morning

Get up about 9 a.m., earlier if you like.

- Detox breakfast.
- Go for a walk, as long as you like.
- Rearrange your own personal space, or part of it if large, to suit yourself better, using ideas from pages 116–20; e.g., de-clutter surfaces and drawers, move furniture for better energy flow.
- Detox lunch.

Afternoon

- Do some stretching (pages 36–7). or the Sun Salutation Sequence (pages 40–41).
- Write a list of things you'd like to do tomorrow. (Make sure they are all pleasant or motivating things, no chores). Divide this list into two – one half being creative things you can do at home (where you output, e.g., writing a short story, taking photos, playing guitar), the other half non-creative things which you can do at home (where you receive input, e.g., having hair done at home, a reflexology session at home).
- Rest and relax.

Evening

- Detox dinner .
- Bath with relaxing essential oils.
- Massage session.
- Practise correct breathing.
- To bed no later than 10.30 p.m.

Day 3

Morning

Get up about 9a.m., or earlier if you like.

- Detox breakfast.
- Do stretching.
- Go for a long walk at moderate pace. Stop on the way several times to enjoy your surroundings or things that you notice.
- Choose one creative thing to do from yesterday's list.
- Detox lunch.

Afternoon

- Rest.
- Choose something non-creative from yesterday's list and do it.
- Do some forward planning for the rest of your life – personal goals, emotional goals, career goals. Write them down. Pick one and write a plan for achieving it.

Evening

- Detox dinner.
- Bath with relaxing essential oils.
- Practise breathing.
- Read/listen to music.
- Go to bed no later than 10.30 p.m.

appendix

Useful books and addresses are arranged by areas of interest, which are set out according to the order in which they are first mentioned in the book. When writing to organizations for information, a stamped addressed envelope is always appreciated.

Shiatsu

Shiatsu Society of Great Britain
5 Foxcote
Wokingham
Berkshire RG11 3PG
tel 01734 730836

Reflexology

British Reflexology Association
Monks Orchard
Whitbourne
Worcester WR6 5RB
tel 01886 821207

Alexander Technique

The Alexander Technique: an Introductory Guide by C. Stevens (Vermilion, 1996)

Society of Teachers of the Alexander Technique
20 London House
266 Fulham Road
London SW10 9EL
tel 0207 351 0828

Pilates

Pilates Through the Day (series) by Lynne Robinson, Helge Fisher and Gordon Thomson
(Pan books, £2.99 each)

The Body Control Pilates Association
14 Neal's Yard
London WC2H 9DP
(send SAE for list of qualified teachers)
tel 0207 379 3734
www.bodycontrol.co.uk

Yoga

British Wheel of Yoga
1 Hamilton Place
Boston Road,
Sleaford
Lincs NG34 7ES
tel 01529 306851

Transcendental Meditation
Freepost
London SW1P 4YY
tel 0990 143733

Yoga Weekends and Holidays

Simon Low
134 Regents Park Road
London NW1 8XL
(send SAE)

Massage

Healing Massage by Susan Mumford
(Hamlyn, £14.99)

Pocket Massage for Stress Relief, Clare Maxwell-Hudson
(Dorling Kindersley, £5.99)

British Federation of Massage Practitioners
78 Meadow Street
Preston
Lancashire PR1 1TS
tel 01772 881063

Massage Therapy Institute of Great Britain (MTIGB)
PO Box 2726
London NW2 3NR
(send SAE for register of members)
tel 0208 208 1607

Manual Lymph Drainage UK
P O Box 149, Wallingford
Oxfordshire OX10 7LD
tel 01865 340337

Aromatherapy

The Complete Illustrated Guide to Aromatherapy by Julia Lawless (Element, £18.99)

The Aromatherapy Organisations Council
PO Box 19834, London SE25 6WF
tel 0208 251 7912
fax 0208 251 7942

General Therapies

British Complementary Medicine Association
Kensington House
33 Imperial Square
Cheltenham
Glos GL50 1QZ
tel 01242 519911

Clinics Practising Complementary Therapies

The Hale Clinic
7 Park Crescent
London W1N 3HE
tel 0207 631 0156

Balance
250 Kings Road
London SW3 5UF
tel 0207 565 0333

Health Farms and Retreats

The Good Retreat Guide by Stafford and Whiteaker
(Vintage/Ebury, £12.99)

Tyringham Naturopathic Clinic
Newport Pagnell
Bucks MK16 9ER
tel 01908 610450

Springs Health Farm
Packington
Ashby de la Zouch
Leics LE65 1TG
tel 01530 273873

Central Booking/Information Agency for Most Health Farms, Spas, etc:

Healthy Venues
45 Armorial Road
Coventry
Warwickshire CV3 6GH
tel 02476 690300
www.healthyvenues.co.uk

Counselling, Health and Mental Health

The British Association for Counselling
1 Regent Place
Rugby
Warwickshire CV21 2PJ
tel 01788 578328
(send SAE for free booklet detailing counsellors area by area)

Friendship of Depressives Anonymous
Box FDA, Ormiston House
32–36 Pelham St
Nottingham NG1 2EG
tel 01702 433 838

SAD (Seasonal Affective Disorder) Association
PO Box 989
Steyning W. Sussex BN44 3NG
(send SAE for details)

The ME Association
4 Corringham Road
Stamford-le-Hope
Essex SS17 OAH
tel 01375 642466/ (information line) 361013

Sport and Exercise

The English Sports Council
16 Upper Woburn Place
London WC1H 0QP
tel 0207 273 1500

Exercise England
Solecast House
13–27 Brunswick Place
London N1 6DX
tel 0870 7506506

National Register of Personal Fitness Trainers
Thornton House
Thornton Road
London SW19 4NG
tel 0208 944 6688

Nutrition and Sports Nutrition

The Food Bible by Judith Wills (Quadrille, p/b £10.99)

Sports Nutrition for Women by Anita Bean (A and C Black, £12.99)

British Dietetic Association
5th floor,
Elizabeth House
22 Suffolk St,
Queensway
Birmingham B1 1LS
tel 0121 616 4900

Society for the Promotion of Nutritional Therapy
PO Box 47
Healthfield
East Sussex TN21 8ZX
(send SAE plus £1 for register of members)
tel 01435 867007

Environment

The Feng Shui Handbook by Lam Kam Chuen (Gaia, £12.99)

Thomas Coxon Associates
(Feng Shui consultants)
26 Mere Road
Wigston Magna
Leicestershire LE18 3RJ
tel 0116 288 6068

The International Association for Colour Therapy
PO Box 3688
London SW13 0NX
tel 0181 878 5276

Relationships

The Relate Guide to Better Relationships by Sarah Litvinoff (Vermilion, £9.99)

Relate
Herbert Gray College
Little Church St, Rugby
Warwickshire CV21 3AP
tel 01788 573241

Drawing Down the Moon
(personal introduction consultants)
Adam and Eve Mews,
London W8 6SH
tel 0207 937 6263
www.drawingdownthemoon.co.uk

Self-improvement/-knowledge

How to Survive Without Psychotherapy by David Smail (Constable, £9.99)

Your Body Speaks Your Mind by Debbie Shapiro (Piatkus, £10.99)

Life Coaching by Eileen Mulligan (Piatkus, £8.99)

Escape
Tregeraint House
Zennor, St Ives
Cornwall TR26 3DB
tel 01736 797061
(send SAE for details)

index

R

S

T

V

W

Y

Z

The author would like to thank the staff of Quadrille for their hard work, and give special thanks to Jane Turnbull, Lewis Esson, Sue Storey and Claire Bowles.